SPEND
SAVE IT?

C000151202

A simple and comprehensive illustrated guide to the coins in your pocket

by Phil Mussell
and the Production Team of COIN NEWS

Published by
Token Publishing Limited

In association with
The Royal Mint

© 2019 Token Publishing Ltd,
40 Southernhay East, Exeter, EX1 1PE
Telephone 01404 46972 email info@tokenpublishing.com
www.tokenpublishing.com

ISBN 978-1-908828-47-7

Printed in Buxton, Derbyshire
by Buxton Press, five times winner of the coveted Printer of the Year award

Distributed to the Newstrade by
Select Publisher Services Ltd, 62 Wimborne Road, Bournemouth BH3 7AR

Like us on Facebook:
facebook.com/TokenPublishing

Follow us on Twitter:
twitter.com/@coinsandmedals

Hello!

WELCOME to the second issue of *Spend it? Save it?* your guide to the coins in your purse and pocket from Token Publishing Ltd. Some of you will be buying this little "bookazine" (not quite a book, not quite a magazine) having purchased the first edition and you want to see what's new out there, whilst others will be buying it for the first time—either way we hope it helps you with your collecting. There has been a huge surge in people collecting "circulating" coins in recent years (that's the coins you find in your change every day), helped at first by the 29 coins of the 2012 Olympic 50p series (did you know one of these could be worth as much as £750 maybe more? We'll tell you which one in this book!) and more recently by the Beatrix Potter and Paddington coins that everybody is looking for and the 10p coins that nobody can seem to find because they are all being squirrelled away! This interest has led to a whole new generation of people checking their change for the rarities—some are doing it in the hope of making some money in an on-line auction, others are doing it because they want a full set, because, whether they have realised it or not they have become coin collectors!

As the interest in circulating coins has increased so too have the urban myths grown up about which ones are worth serious money, which ones can't be found, etc., so we at Token Publishing Ltd thought it would be a good idea that there was somewhere you could go to find out what coins you should be looking out for and what they're really worth, not just an on-line resource written by somebody who doesn't know but a proper price guide written by people who have been involved in coin collecting for

over 35 years—we have been publishing a monthly magazine on coins called COIN NEWS for over three decades so we like to think we know what we are talking about!

Whatever your reason for collecting we hope you have fun with it. The thing to remember about collecting coins is that yes, some are worth a lot of money and if you manage to find one in your change you could certainly sell it for a lot more than face value (we'll tell you which ones they are later!) but not every coin you find is going to be valuable—but that doesn't really matter because they are still lots of fun to collect and if nothing else it's a great way to save!

You also have to remember not to believe everything you hear about some of the silly prices people claim things are worth—there is no circulating modern British coin out there today worth more than about £800–1,000, but as that one is a 2p that's a pretty decent profit! Which 2p is it? Well you'll have to read on to find out.

Inside these pages you'll find a full guide to all the coins in circulation today (and some that shouldn't be), as well as information telling you what to look out for and what your coins are worth—and most importantly you will find out what the real rarities are, so when you find something a bit unusual, do you Spend it? or do you Save it? This book will tell you what to do.

There's also a really useful cut-out-and-keep section at the back that allows you to tick off the coins you've got, so you'll know what to look out for when you next have a pocketful of change—happy hunting!

In this issue

The rare Kew Gardens 50p

The 12-sided £1

How
did we get to where we are today?

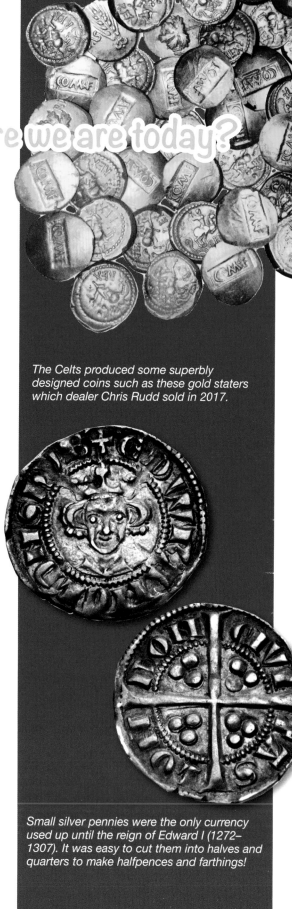

Coins have been in use for 1000s of years, they first came about in Lydia (in what is modern day Turkey) in the 7th Century BC when the king, Alyattes, put his mark (the head of a lion) on lumps of electrum (a mixture of gold and silver) to reassure people that they could exchange them for goods because they really were precious metal and not something ordinary and valueless. In what was eventually to become Britain, the earliest coins were those of the Celtic tribes and the Romans—they were bronze, silver and gold coins meaning that they too were actually made of precious metal, the mark of the tribe or the head of the Emperor proved that, if somebody faked that mark they were punished severely. After the Romans left in around AD 400 we entered what was known as the Dark Ages and our coins did too—for nearly 1,000 years all we had were silver pennies: that was it. There were some gold coins around but they weren't used every day, they tended just to be used for offerings, tributes and really big transactions—everybody else just used pennies (these often had crosses on them and as they were so thin because of the way they were made they could be cut along the crosses to make half a penny or a quarter of a penny).

The Celts produced some superbly designed coins such as these gold staters which dealer Chris Rudd sold in 2017.

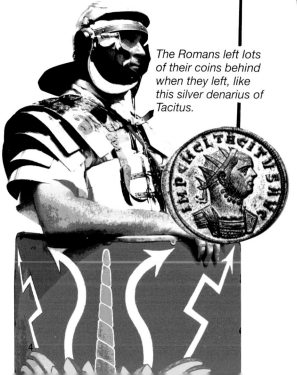

The Romans left lots of their coins behind when they left, like this silver denarius of Tacitus.

Small silver pennies were the only currency used up until the reign of Edward I (1272–1307). It was easy to cut them into halves and quarters to make halfpences and farthings!

Before we went "Decimal",
in one pound (£1) there were:

960 farthings
or 480 halfpences
or 240 pennies
or 80 threepences
or 40 sixpences
or 20 shillings
or 10 florins
or 8 halfcrowns
or 4 crowns

It wasn't until the reign of Edward I (1272–1307) that other coins were introduced when he brought in the farthing (quarter of a penny), the halfpenny and the groat (four pence). It was Edward III (1327–77) that brought in circulating gold coins (the noble, half noble and quarter noble) and from this time right up until the 20th century, Britain (and the countries/kingdoms that made it up over the years) used the same basic system of coinage divided up into pounds, shillings and pence with the pound being worth 20 shillings and a shilling being worth 12 pence, meaning there were 240 pennies in a pound. Over the years there have been all sorts of coins minted—we've always had a penny, but there were also farthings, halfpennies, threepences, groats, sixpences, shillings, halfcrowns (two and a half shillings) and crowns (five shillings). In the larger denominations (which were usually gold coins) we have had nobles, sovereigns (which could be worth as much as 30 shillings depending on the price of gold), angels, ryals, crowns, laurels, unites, guineas and the modern sovereign (which had its value pegged at 20 shillings or one pound)—but whatever the coin was called it was always based on the principle of pounds, shillings and pence.

READ ON ▶

Throughout history Britain has had some wonderful coins including those illustrated here, but all were based on the fact that there were 240 pennies in one pound. The coins above can all be found on the website of Sovereign Rarities of London, www.sovr.co.uk

11s	55p	16s	80p
12s	60p	17s	85p
13s	65p	18s	90p
14s	70p	19s	95p
15s	75p	£1	100p

However, everything changed in the second half of the 20th century when it was decided that the whole thing was needlessly complicated and that something simpler was needed. The new system that was decided on had already been adopted across most of Europe and in the USA and was far more logical and straightforward. It was the "base ten" system, with 100 small units making up a larger unit. For example, in the USA it was 100 cents making up a dollar, in France 100 centimes made up a Franc (this was before the Euro—but that uses base ten too with 100 Eurocents making one Euro) and in the UK it was to be 100 pennies in a pound. Because the old pounds, shillings and pence coins were no longer needed new coins were to be minted that worked on base ten: the new 50p coin was to be worth half a pound, a 10p was worth a tenth of a pound and so on. There was to be no shilling, no sixpence, no threepence, no halfcrown (the crown denomination was kept and is still used today as a commemorative coin although now it has a face value of £5, not the 25p it was originally), no florin, no farthing. The halfpenny was kept at first but inflation meant it didn't last long (see the halfpenny section on page 63). It was to be a real challenge for the country and a lot of preparation went in to making sure it all went smoothly.

The day this was all to change was set as February 15, 1971, and it was known as Decimalisation Day or D-Day (Decimal from the Latin *decimus* meaning tenth). Before then the people of the UK had been getting ready for the changeover with a huge marketing campaign and some of the new coins were introduced early—from 1968 a new 10p coin was minted to be used alongside the florin (two shillings) and a 5p coin was introduced as it had the same face value as the shilling. In addition a 50p, the first seven-sided coin, was introduced to be used instead of the existing ten shilling note.

These new coins had the words "New Pence" on them to differentiate between them and the "old" money. After Decimal Day the old shillings and florins could still be used (as a 5p and 10p) but you couldn't use a ten shilling note as the shilling was no longer a denomination. You could, actually, still use the sixpence which was valued at 2½p and continued to be legal tender right up until June 30, 1980. Incidentally, the Royal Mint still makes sixpences—they

Cadbury's decimal coin MILK CHOCOLATE

started minting them again in 2016 as the "lucky sixpence" (Brides are meant to wear them in their shoes, according to the rhyme "something old, something new, something borrowed, something blue and a silver sixpence in her shoe") but they aren't really circulating coins so aren't covered in this bookazine.

In 1971 the first "New Pence" coins were the half penny, the penny, the two pence, five pence, ten pence and fifty pence with notes for £1, £5, £10 and £20 (a £50 note was introduced a bit later). In 1982 the 20p coin was introduced and in 1983 the £1 coin followed (eventually taking the place of the £1 note). The £2 coin was introduced first as a commemorative in 1986 and then as a circulating coin in 1997. The standard designs of the coins (excluding the special issues of the 50p and the £2 and the £1 coin which changed regularly) remained the same with a separate heraldic theme on each coin (the lion of England

on the 10p, the thistle of Scotland on the 5p, the Prince of Wales feathers on the 2p and so on) right up until 2008 when the Royal Mint held a competition to redesign our nation's coins completely.

The competition was won by Matthew Dent who designed the coins so that the smaller coins from 1p to 50p would all come together like a jigsaw puzzle to form the Shield of Arms—the Shield itself would appear on the £1 coin. Did you know that's what the designs were supposed to do? Take a look at page 9 and then see if you can make the shield yourself! Since then there have been a number of changes to the coins: the "round pound" has gone and we now have a 12-sided one instead and there's a 10p series bearing letters of the alphabet (all these are covered later on!), but the basic designs remain the same and there are always at least some of the "standard" coins minted every year.

Dateline

Britain goes decimal

1971

BRITAIN'S FIRST DECIMAL COINS

Britain's new decimal coinage breaks away from a system of counting coins dating back to Anglo-Saxon times. There are three bronze coins (the ½, 1 and 2 new penny) and two cupro-nickel coins (the 5 and 10 new penny).

The obverse (by Mr. Arnold Machin, O.B.E., R.A.) shows the Queen wearing a diamond tiara, a wedding present from Queen Mary. This portrait is also used by Australia, Canada and New Zealand.

The reverse designs are by Mr. Christopher Ironside. Their heraldic descriptions are:
½p The Royal Crown.
1p A Portcullis with chains royally crowned, originally a badge of King Henry VII, but for long closely associated with the Palace of Westminster.
2p The badge of the Prince of Wales. Three ostrich feathers enfiling a coronet of crosses pattée and fleurs de lys, with the motto "Ich Dien."
5p The badge of Scotland. A thistle royally crowned.
10p Part of the crest of England. A lion passant guardant royally crowned.

1982

We drop the word "NEW" and add the 20p, the next year the "round" pound is introduced

1986

A £2 coin is introduced. At first it is all one metal but in 1997 the bi-metallic £2 is launched

The current Shield series arrives

2008

The winning set was designed by Matthew Dent, who had seen the competition advertised in a newspaper.

2017

Then in 2017 we have the current bi-metallic 12-sided £1

Scarce vs. rare

When is a coin rare? When is it scarce? And if it's neither why can't you find one of them in your change!?

We've all seen the tables on-line and in the newspapers, the really useful guides that tell you how scarce a coin is. They work it out by taking information on mintages as well as asking the general public how often they come across the coins, and then produce tables letting us know how likely it is that we are going to come across a Scouting 50p or an NHS one, or maybe one of the alphabet 10p coins. Because of the way they work, getting information from the general public who are actively looking for coins, they are a good way of telling what is around and what isn't. BUT they DO NOT tell you how rare an actual coin is, only how easy, or difficult, it is to find and the two things must not be confused.

For example on the Change Checker Scarcity Index for the 50p, most coins are where you would think they would be, with the coins that have the lowest mintages (number of coins made) being listed as the "scarcest" and the ones with higher mintages being most common—that makes perfect sense. However, it's not as simple as that—quite a lot of the coins that seem to be "scarce" actually have quite high mintages and those that seem to be more common were struck in lower volumes—but how can this be? Surely a coin with a lower mintage must be scarcer, no? Well no not always—this is simply because of the number of people who are collecting them. Yes, there are some people who are trying to get "one of everything" and will pull out every 50p, 10p or £2 coin they can, but there are also lots of others who are just collecting, say, the Beatrix Potter 50p coins. This means that although there may be millions of those coins that enter circulation, a lot of them have been taken out and are being stored in albums or jars somewhere, meaning they don't actually "circulate" around the country and so don't find their way in to your change. Others that maybe aren't so eagerly sought after, maybe like the World Wide Fund for Nature 50p or the Battle of Hastings coin seem to appear more regularly

just because not as many people are collecting them—for example there were 9.6 million 2016 Peter Rabbit coins minted and 3.5 million FEWER Battle of Hastings coins struck in the same year—but you will probably find a Hastings one before you find a Peter one as more people have taken Peter out for their own collections!

What is really important to remember is that most modern coins are minted in their millions (we give you the exact figures later) and very few of them can ever be considered "rare". The tables telling you how scarce something is are excellent but they should never be taken as indicators of value (and to be fair the people who produce them never say they should!). All they do is tell you how easy or difficult it is to find a particular coin and just because something is "scarcer" one week that doesn't mean it will be impossible to find. This is really important to remember, scarce does not mean rare and it certainly doesn't mean valuable, so please don't pay way over the odds for a coin just because it isn't that easy to find.

It's perfectly OK to pay a few pounds for a good condition circulating coin that you just can't find if you really want it to complete your set. But just because you might be prepared to pay more than face value for something, that doesn't mean it is actually worth that amount. It might be that when you come to sell no-one is looking for that particular coin so they won't be interested in paying you the same amount that you paid for it. No coin dealer is going to give you more than face value for a used coin when there are millions of others exactly the same out there in circulation . . . and don't forget, the better the condition of a coin the higher the value—coins in as-new condition are worth far more than worn ones. Many of the coins in circulation are also struck in precious metals specially for collectors—but that is a whole new area to consider!

IMPORTANT!

The prices given in the charts in this publication are the figures you should expect to PAY for a coin in first class condition (or EF—Extremely Fine in numismatic terms). If you are SELLING your coin you should expect to be offered less, around 50-75% of that figure. However, not every dealer will be interested in buying your coins as most already have large stocks and others only deal in antique coins. If the coin is in any way worn or marked then it will be worth considerably less than the figures given. REMEMBER: Coins should *never* be cleaned, except with soap and water!

A note on coloured coins

When the Royal Mint released the circulating children's classics 50 pence coins in cupro-nickel they also minted a limited number in solid silver, which then had the character (be it Peter Rabbit or Paddington) coloured in. Recently we have noticed that a number of "coloured" coins are appearing online but these are NOT silver—these are standard circulating coins that have been coloured up using a decal (sticker). There's nothing wrong with this and indeed the seller is selling them as ordinary 50p coins that he has colourised. He is breaking no law and, to be honest, they look rather fetching, BUT there is always a danger that these things will appear in the months and years to come as silver, with unscrupulous people trying to fool the public—so buyer beware!

There are three rules to buying more expensive silver and gold coins and you should follow them if you don't want to lose out: (1) Only buy from a reputable company/dealer. (2) Try and buy coins in the original packaging if you can—in this case the Royal Mint has never sold the coloured 50p coins just on their own, they are always neatly and nicely packaged. (3) If something looks too good to be true then it usually is and buying a solid silver coin for just a few pounds would definitely qualify in that category!

LOOK OUT!

Genuine coloured coins from the Royal Mint are very attractive and are pure silver—don't get caught by buying ordinary coins that have been coloured after their manufacture.

Beware
"buy it now" and crazy bidding on-line

Part of the problem these days is you will often see quotes on websites and in newspapers saying that "such and such rare coin" has been listed on-line for £1,000, £2,000, £10,000 or whatever, and then they go on about how this is a record, etc., etc. That's great, but it is also meaningless.

Firstly, just because something is listed at a certain price that doesn't mean it is worth that or will indeed sell for that. I could put a broken pencil online with a buy it now figure of £1,000 (or more) if I wanted to but it would be, ahem, pointless (sorry!). I certainly wouldn't get £1,000 for it. In fact I wouldn't sell that pencil at all. All I am doing is wasting my time so why would I bother? Well I'm afraid a lot of the time people list things at silly prices because they are trying to scam you. What happens is that someone will list a coin for £1,000 knowing they won't sell it, but then they withdraw the coin, say it is no longer for sale and make people think it sold for £1,000. They then list a similar coin for a much lower price (say £25). It won't even be worth the £25 but as someone has seen it on line for £1,000 and that it "sold" for that, they think £25 is a bargain and they buy it—they then end up with a coin that's worth just face value because they were too caught up with thinking they have bought something cheap.

The only sure way to not get caught out is to find out exactly what the coin you want is worth. Shop around, talk to other collectors and read bookazines like this—that way you'll know exactly what you should be paying if you can't find the coin you want in your change.

Don't be fooled, either by crazy bidding or apparent sales. Sometimes you will see coins that have been bid up to silly money but usually such things won't actually sell, often it's just people playing about by pushing the price up for a laugh and whilst the auction sites do all they can to stop this they can't prevent it all the time.

So, please remember—just because a coin is listed at a certain price that doesn't mean it is worth it and just because something seems to have sold for a certain amount that doesn't mean it actually did. Most importantly remember that just because you buy something at a certain price that doesn't mean you'll be able to sell it for the same money—it all depends on the market at the time and who is interested in buying what! Oh, and please remember, it isn't all just about how much something is worth—coin collecting can be a whole lot of fun too!

IMPORTANT!

The prices given in the charts in this publication are the figures you should expect to **PAY** for a coin in first class condition (or **EF**—Extremely Fine in numismatic terms). If you are **SELLING** your coin you should expect to be offered far less, around 50-75% of that figure. However, not every dealer will be interested in buying your coins as most already have large stocks and others only deal in antique coins. If the coin is in any way worn or marked then it will be worth considerably less than the figures given.

A note on
ERRORS/ODDITIES

The Royal Mint makes literally billions of coins a year, if you ever get a chance to go to the Royal Mint Experience in Llantrisant, South Wales you will see the machines pumping out hundreds of coins a minute. In this, like any automated manufacturing process, the odd error creeps in every now and then and whilst the Mint's quality control is excellent these errors sometimes get out.

Every so often you will find coins that have the heads and tails sides at differing angles to each other where one of the two dies that are used to produce the coins has slipped round (so when you hold the heads side upright the tails side is at an angle instead of being straight), or perhaps you will find a coin that is struck a little off-centre, that sort of thing. These are not the same kind of "error" that produced coins like the dateless 20p (see the 20p section on page 50) they are simply an inevitable part of manufacturing, but people do collect them all the same and they will fetch more than face value if in good condition. Although our advice is if you find an error, keep it—it's an interesting piece in its own right (the reason they are collected is they happen so rarely—the Mint's quality control will usually spot any mistakes long before they get into circulation). However, if you do want to sell it, then putting it into auction (either a "real" auction or on-line) will probably be the best way to determine its value, although a dealer may well offer you a good price if he or she has a buyer for errors.

One error that has cropped up in recent months is the new £1 coin struck on an old £1 coin blank (meaning it is 12-sided but looks all gold and not bi-metallic). These have been appearing on-line and, as far as we can tell, are genuine errors. There is no indication of how many might have "escaped" but they are fetching quite large sums.

As these errors are unintentional and the numbers made are never recorded (if the Mint knew about them they would prevent them leaving the factory floor), it is impossible to place a true value on them, especially as every error is different! As such they are not individually included in this price guide.

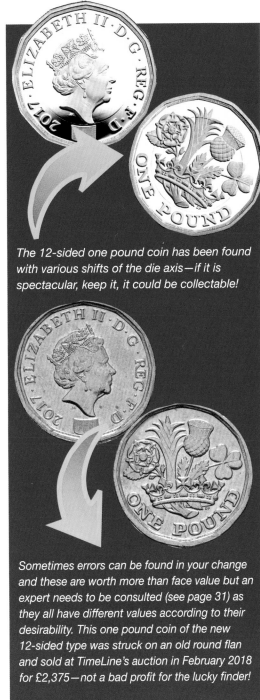

The 12-sided one pound coin has been found with various shifts of the die axis—if it is spectacular, keep it, it could be collectable!

Sometimes errors can be found in your change and these are worth more than face value but an expert needs to be consulted (see page 31) as they all have different values according to their desirability. This one pound coin of the new 12-sided type was struck on an old round flan and sold at TimeLine's auction in February 2018 for £2,375—not a bad profit for the lucky finder!

Circulating vs non-circulating vs Commemorative

There's often confusion about what a "circulating" coin actually is and what other coins are if they aren't struck to be spent—and sometimes the lines get so blurred it's not that easy to tell which is which.

In general a circulating coin is one minted for us to spend, to use as money. These coins are sent from the Royal Mint in Llantrisant in Wales to the banks, the banks then send them out to shops and the general public. These are the coins that we see every day and the ones most of you will be looking through to add to your collections.

The so called "non-circulating" coins are the same as the circulating ones—they will be the 50p coins, the £2 coins and are made of the same metal as the standard coins but, for whatever reason, they don't go to the banks to be sent out for general use. In some cases, like with the Gruffalo or Stephen Hawking 50p (above), they were minted especially for collectors and were never intended to go into circulation, but others, like the Jane Austen (top right) or Aviation £2 coins from 2017, never got sent out because there were already enough £2 coins in the system and they simply weren't needed. You can still buy them in collector packs but you won't usually find them in your change. You will find that these "non-circulating" coins are included in this book because, believe it or not, they do sometimes find their way into circulation. People break open the packs and spend the coins—if you find one it will certainly be worth more than face value. But don't go too mad—those "non-circulating" coins that do find their way into our

pockets may well seem rare but they will never be worth more than the same uncirculated coin in a pack which you can buy from a coin dealer or from the Royal Mint!

Commemorative coins are different again, these are coins that are never meant for circulation at all and are minted solely for the coin collector market. These may be the standard denominations (50p, £1, £2, etc.) but minted in a precious metal such as gold or silver, or they may be £5 coins (or crowns). These crowns come in both "base metal" (usually cupro-nickel) or precious metal and are minted for special occasions like Royal Weddings or births and yes they are officially "legal tender" but all that really means is that you can use them to pay a fine in court but shops, as a rule, don't like to take them. You'd be silly to spend one anyway as generally they are worth much more than face value to collectors. Because of this we don't include them in this book but they are included in its sister volume the COIN YEARBOOK.

WHAT does that mean?

Occasionally in the world of coins you'll hear some terms you aren't familiar with, so here's a quick guide:

Obverse —
This is the Heads side and will show a portrait of Her Majesty Queen Elizabeth II.

Reverse —
This is the Tails side and it is this you'll be looking out for. It is the reverse of the coins that makes them different from each other.

Proof Coins —
These are specially struck and have a different look to ordinary coins, sometimes they will have a mirrored background and a frosted design, other times they will have colour on them. Often they are made of precious metals—you don't normally find them in change. However, if you do, save them, don't spend them, particularly if they might be real silver!

Circulating Coins —
The everyday coins you find in your purse or pocket, the ones you get in change. Rather confusingly you can have an uncirculated circulating coin! Uncirculated refers to the condition (see below), circulating just means coins like it are the ones we use every day.

Commemorative Coins —
These are specially struck coins to commemorate an event, like the £5 coin struck for the Royal Wedding recently. You don't find these in change so they aren't covered in this book. Some of the coins you do find—like the Scout and Guide 50ps or the NHS 50p—are struck for an anniversary but they aren't referred to as commemorative coins.

Grading (Condition)

The condition of your coin is really important, the better condition the more it's worth (and the more you'll pay for it if you get fed up with waiting for one in change). Here's what the different grades mean:

BU or Brilliant Uncirculated —
These are coins that look like they've just come from the Royal Mint, they haven't been touched by human hands and are usually found in protective packaging, these are "Mint" coins. If a coin looks like it is "uncirculated" but you find it in change (meaning it has been in circulation—has to be because you have one!) then it will be classed as EF or VF (see below). BU coins are the ones everybody wants because they are the best condition.

EF or Extremely Fine —
A coin that looks like it hasn't been circulated but if you've found it in your purse or pocket it must have been, it can't be classed as "uncirculated" but it looks like it is. These will be worth a bit less than uncirculated coins unless they are very rare—most collectors will realise that they won't be able to get a BU coin (because they are looking for them in change) and so will be hoping for an EF one.

VF or Very Fine —
One step down from EF, this coin will still look pretty good but it may have a bit of wear because it has been in circulation for a while.

F or Fine —
If a coin has been around for some time the chances are it will have worn a bit. Most of the coins you find in your pocket will be "Fine" (or even lower grade) just because they've been used by hundreds if not thousands of people over the years and they've been bashed about next to other coins in tills, purses, pockets, piggy banks, etc.

Fair —
These coins are lower even than "Fine". They've seen some action and are looking a bit worse for wear—sadly no one is really going to love them unless they are really rare and no circulating coins today are really rare.

Poor —
You'll know a "poor" coin when you see one, it will be bashed about and generally in a bad way— holed or worn smooth coins are in this category. No collector will want it unless it's a real rarity and even then it won't fetch anywhere near the money a better example would. Luckily we don't see many "poor" coins these days, if they are really bashed about they get taken out of circulation pretty quickly and none of our coins have been around long enough to be worn smooth!

TWO POUNDS

The first ones

Specifications

Diameter	28.4mm
Weight	12.0g
Thickness	2.50mm
Composition	Nickel-Brass
	(76% copper, 4% nickel, 20% zinc)
Edge	Milled with edge inscription

1986
Commonwealth Games

1989
Bill of Rights

1989
Claim of Right

1994
Tercentenary of the
Bank of England

1995
Anniversary of WWII

1995
Founding of the
United Nations

1996
European Football
Championship

The £2 coin was originally introduced in 1986 as a commemorative coin to celebrate the Commonwealth Games of that year, but unlike the £2 coins we all know today, this wasn't produced as a bi-metallic coin and was all one colour using one metal (nickel brass), although silver and gold versions were minted too.

Two more nickel brass coins were produced three years later to celebrate the Tercentenary (300) years of the Bill of Rights and the Tercentenary of the Claim of Right. Another followed in 1994 to celebrate the Tercentenary of the Bank of England, then the next year there was one to commemorate the 50th anniversary of the end of World War II and one to celebrate the 50th anniversary of the founding of the United Nations.

In 1996 another was struck to celebrate the European Football Championships that were being held in England that year—that was the last one before the bi-metallic coin was introduced. However, you are unlikely to find any of these in your change as they were seldom used as circulating coins and whilst they had the value of £2, shops generally wouldn't accept them.

TWO POUNDS

The current ones

There are two "Standard" reverses on the £2 coins.

Specifications

Diameter	28.4mm
Weight	12.0g
Thickness	2.50mm
Composition	Outer: Nickel-Brass
	(76% copper, 4% nickel, 20% zinc)
	Inner: Cupro-nickel
	(75% copper, 25% nickel)
Edge	Milled with edge inscription

The first of the £2 coins as we know them today were issued in 1997—or at least they were supposed to be! The design (the standard one we refer to as the technology design) was released early in 1997 but then the coins never followed. It appears there was something wrong with the "electronic signature" of the coin (the thing that tells vending machines, parking meters, etc., what it is) and so the coins were withheld until the following year when all 13 million of them that had been prepared were launched into general circulation.

As well as seeing all the new £2 coins being released, 1998 also saw another change to the coinage when Raphael Maklouf's portrait of Her Majesty the Queen on the obverse (heads) side of the coin was changed for a new portrait of the Queen by Ian Rank-Broadley. All coins issued with the 1998 date had this new portrait on and that meant that there was only one issue showing the Queen "with the necklace" (the Maklouf portrait showed her wearing a necklace, but the Rank-Broadley one showed a different view with the head taking up most of the coin with no room for much of her neck or shoulders—and certainly no necklace). Because there was only ever one striking of the circulating £2 coin showing the Maklouf bust an urban myth has grown up around the 1997 coin's value, with people believing it to be worth far more than just £2. It isn't. There were millions of them minted and millions are still

out there, not as many as the ones that showed the Ian Rank-Broadley portrait so yes, there are fewer of them around but still far, far, more than is necessary to make them collectable and valuable.

The scarcest £2 coins are the 2002 Commonwealth Games Coins—in that year four separate coins were minted which all look alike (with the design of an athlete "breaking the tape") but which had one very important difference between them—next to the athlete was a little circle which showed a flag representing each of the Home nations: England, Scotland, Northern Ireland and Wales. Of these, Northern Ireland is the scarcest with fewer than 500,000 minted—an uncirculated one of these will certainly be worth more than face value!

After the Commonwealth Games coins the rarest £2s are the 2015 Anniversary of World War I and the 2015 Britannia with the new Queen's portrait by Jody Clark on it, but there were still 650,000 each of those put into circulation so they can't really be called "rare" and aren't going to make you a fortune. However, if you have an uncirculated example it will probably fetch more than face value. Two of the "rarest" in terms of finding them in your change are the 2008 and 2012 "Olympics Handover" coins—there were around 850,000 of each minted but a lot of people kept them as souvenirs. There aren't that many around so they are good ones to look out for!

What's it worth?

DATE	Mintage	Value
First £2 coins, in nickel-brass:		
1986 Commonwealth Games	8,212,184	£5
1989 Tercentenary of Bill of Rights	4,392,825	£10
1989 Tercentenary of Claim of Right (only issued in Scotland)	381,400	£30
1994 Tercentenary of the Bank of England	1,443,116	£10
1995 50th Anniversary of End of WWII	4,394,566	£10
1995 50th Anniversary of the United Nations	1,668,575	£10
1996 European Football Championships	5,195,350	£10
Bi-metallic issue introduced with a standard design with the edge reading "Standing on the shoulders of Giants"		
1997 Standard design	13,734,625	£5
1998 Standard design	91,110,375	£4
1999 Standard design	33,719,000	£4
1999 Rugby World Cup	4,933,000	£6
2000 Standard design	25,770,000	£4
2001 Standard design	34,984,750	£4
2001 Marconi	4,558,000	£5
2002 Standard design	13,024,750	£4
2002 Commonwealth Games		
— Scotland	771,750	£15
— Wales	558,500	£15
— Northern Ireland	485,500	£30
— England	650,500	£15

1989—one metal type.
Tercentenary of Claim of Right
(only issued in Scotland)

FUN FACT!

Few people had even heard of the Bill of Rights or the Claim of Right until the coins were issued in 1989. Go on, Google it!

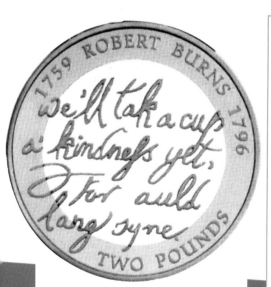

2009—bi-metal type.
250th Anniversary of birth of
Robert Burns

	Mintage	Value
2003 Standard design	17,531,250	£4
2003 DNA Double Helix	4,299,000	£5
2004 Standard design	11,981,500	£4
2004 Trevithick Steam Locomotive	5,004,500	£5
2005 Standard design	3,837,250	£4
2005 Gunpowder Plot	5,140,500	£5
2005 End of World War II	10,191,000	£5
2006 Standard design	16,715,000	£4
2006 Brunel, The Man (Portrait)	7,928,250	£5
2006 Brunel, His Achievements (Paddington Station)	7,452,250	£5
2007 Standard design	10,270,000	£4
2007 Tercentenary of the Act of Union	7,545,000	£5
2007 Bicentenary of the Abolition of the Slave Trade	8,445,000	£8
2008 Standard design	30,107,000	£4
2008 Centenary of 4th Olympiad, London	910,000	£8
2008 Olympic Games Handover Ceremony	918,000	£8
2009 Standard design	8,775,000	£4
2009 250th Anniversary of birth of Robert Burns	3,253,000	£5
2009 200th Anniversary of birth of Charles Darwin	3,903,000	£5

What's it worth?

DATE	Mintage	Value
2010 Standard design	6,890,000	£4
2010 Florence Nightingale 150 Years of Nursing	6,175,000	£4
2011 Standard design	24,375,030	£4
2011 500th Anniversary of the Mary Rose	1,040,000	£10
2011 400th Anniversary of the King James Bible	975,000	£10
2012 Standard design	3,900,000	£3
2012 200th Anniversary of birth of Charles Dickens	8,190,000	£4
2012 Olympic Handover to Rio	845,000	£8
2013 Standard design	15,860,250	£4
2013 150th Anniversary of the London Underground		
— Roundel design	1,560,000	£6
— Train design	1,690,000	£6
2013 350th Anniversary of the Guinea	2,990,000	£5
2014 Standard design	18,200,000	£4
2014 100th Anniversary of the Outbreak of WWI	5,720,000	£4
2014 500th Anniversary of Trinity House	3,705,000	£4
2015 Standard design	35,360,058	£4
2015 Anniversary of WWI—Royal Navy	650,000	£10
2015 800th Anniversary of Magna Carta	1,495,000	£15
2015 New Britannia standard design	650,000	£6

£2

2012
200th Anniversary of birth of
Charles Dickens

Did you know?

Many of the later more expensive coins were originally only issued in special packs or as part of the Royal Mint Year Sets.

1914 · 1918

THE WAR IN THE AIR

HDG

2017
100th Anniversary of WWI: Aviation

	Mintage	Value
2016 Standard Britannia design	2,925,000	£5
2016 400th Anniversary of Shakespeare's death		
— Comedies	4,355,000	£4
— Tragedies	4,615,000	£4
— Histories	5,655,000	£4
2016 350th Anniversary of the Great Fire of London	1,625,000	£4
2016 Anniversary of WWI—Army	9,550,000	£4
2017 Standard Britannia design	—	£5
2017 Anniversary of WWI—Aviation	—	£10
2017 150th Anniversary of Jane Austen	—	£10
2018 Standard Britannia design	—	£3
2018 Centenary of the RAF		
— Badge	—	£10
— Spitfire	—	£10
— Vulcan	—	£10
— Sea King	—	£10
— Lightning II	—	£10
2018 Journey to Armistice	—	£10
2018 250th Anniversary of Captain Cook's "Voyage of Discovery"—I	—	£10
2018 Bicentenary of Mary Shelley's "Frankenstein"	—	£12
2019 260th Anniversary of Wedgwood	—	£10
2019 350th Anniversary of Samuel Pepys' Last diary entry	—	£10
2019 75th Anniversary of D-Day	—	£10
2019 250th Anniversary of Captain Cook—II	—	£10

British Coinage

1997–2015
The standard design
representing "Technology"

1999
Rugby World Cup

2001
Centenary of wireless
transmission across the
Atlantic

2002
Commonwealth Games
(Scotland)

2002
Commonwealth Games
(Wales)

THE
SCARCE
ONE

2002
Commonwealth Games
(Northern Ireland)

2002
Commonwealth Games
(England)

×2 ✓

2003
50th Anniversary of the
Discovery of DNA

2004
200th Anniversary of the
First Steam Locomotive

✓

2005
60th Anniversary of the
End of WWII

2005
400th Anniversary of the
Gunpowder Plot

✓

2006
200th Anniversary of
Brunel—The Man

£2

£2 coin collection 1997–2019

2006
200th Anniversary of
Brunel—His Achievements

2007
300th Anniversary of the
Act of Union

2007
200th Anniversary of
Abolition of the Slave Trade

2008
Centenary of the
4th Olympiad

2008
Olympic Handover:
Beijing to London

2009
200th Anniversary of the
birth of Charles Darwin

2009
250th Anniversary of
Robert Burns

2010
150th Anniversary of
Florence Nightingale

2011
500th Anniversary of the
King James Bible

2011
500th Anniversary of the
Mary Rose

2012
Olympic Handover:
London to Rio

2012
200th Anniversary of
Charles Dickens

£2 coin collection 1997–2019

2013
150th Anniversary of the
London Underground:
Roundel

2013
150th Anniversary of the
London Underground:
Locomotive

2013
350th Anniversary of
the Guinea

2014
100th Anniversary of the
Outbreak of WWI

2014
500th Anniversary of
Trinity House

2015
100th Anniversary of WWI:
The Royal Navy

2015
800th Anniversary of
Magna Carta

2015 on
The standard Britannia
design

2016
350th Anniversary of the
Great Fire of London

2016
100th Anniversary of WWI:
The Army

2016
400th Anniversary of
Shakespeare's death:
Histories

2016
400th Anniversary of
Shakespeare's death:
Comedies

British Coinage

£2 coin collection 1997–2019

2016
400th Anniversary of
Shakespeare's death:
Tragedies

2017
150th Anniversary of
Jane Austen

2017
100th Anniversary of WWI:
Aviation

2018
Centenary of
the Royal Air Force

2018
Royal Air Force
Spitfire

2018
Royal Air Force
Vulcan

2018
Royal Air Force
Sea King

2018
Royal Air Force
Lightening II

2018
250th Anniversary of
Captain Cook's "Voyage of
Discovery"—I

2018
100th Anniversary of WWI:
Journey to Armistice

2018
200th Anniversary of
Mary Shelley and
"Frankenstein"

2019
260th Anniversary of
Wedgwood

Bi-metallic "errors"...
Scott Wren explains why two is better than one

In light of the new 12-sided £1, now being ingrained into UK circulating coinage, its predecessor, the £2 bi-metallic seems like a hardened veteran of pockets, tills, wallets and purses. However, this veteran has an array of futuristic "errors".

The **Chard** website, https://24carat.co.uk/frame.php?url=1994twopoundsbimetalroyalminttrial.html has a complete synopsis of the production through to striking process of the modern £2 bi-metallic coin, which is well worth a read as a prelude to understanding the evolutionary processes that bring about £2 bi-metallic "errors".

For the sake of uniformity and understanding for you the reader, I will refer to the two "pieces" that comprise the whole, as the "Outer Ring" which is made from Nickel-Brass (NiBr), and an "Inner Core" made of Cupro-Nickel (CuNi).

So, with the aforementioned details established—we can concentrate on the "errors" that occur on the modern £2 . . . *in a nutshell*, the same range of "errors" that affect mono-metallic coins, will affect the bi-metallic examples; it is just that the two separate pieces make for some rather obvious differences in the ensuing "errors" produced, when they finally come together. For the most part, "errors" that predominantly affect only the bi-metallic coin—and which makes them more spectacular than their mono-metallic counterparts—stem from what would be only minor "errors" on mono-metallic coins *but* when incorporated into a bi-metallic coin make for something entirely more spectacular. Prime examples are the "Clipped Planchet" errors or "bitten edge" as seen in **Image 1**, the "inner core" was punched out from the end of the sheet of metal used for blanks and thus formed a "Straight/Ragged Edge Clip"—this occurs from time to time on mono-metallic coins—but once mated/paired with the "outer ring", it exposes a rather large missing space or gap.

Image 2. 2001 £2 "Off-centre Inner Core".

The coin pictured in **Image 2**, as spectacular as it looks, has an explanation for its origin that is a lot simpler. It's the result of the "inner core" not being centred when the coins are mated/united prior to being struck, so the result is an off-centre "inner core" and because of the specific engineering design features of the bi-metallic £2 and the mating process itself, the "inner core" "spills" into the "outer ring" . . . and as you will no doubt agree, the result is quite spectacular. See the aforementioned link to Chard's website on the striking process for the £2, as it discusses dual feeding systems into the striking chamber, one for the "outer ring", and a separate system for the "inner core". The coin in **Image 3** is that of a £2 coin with a "Faulty Planchet/'Outer ring' ", and aside from being a great "error", it effectively shows the composition of the two parts to the bi-metallic coin, and clearly shows

Image 1. 2005 £2 "Ragged/Straight Clipped Inner Core".

the previously referenced "specific engineering design features" in the form of the "grooving" on the "inner core" which assists the metal flow to bond with the "outer ring" at the time of striking to fuse the two parts together.

Image 3. £2 "Faulty Outer Ring".

The *Holy Grail* of bi-metallic "errors", in my personal opinion, are the examples where the bi-metallic coin ends up being *mono*-metallic, the result of the nickel-brass £2 blank not having the "inner core" sized portion punched out to begin with, and the ensuing, entirely nickel-brass, "error" blank finding its way into the striking chamber. The results are you have a full one-piece nickel-brass £2 example that is struck with the complete design on obverse and reverse. The following link to a www.coinworld.com online article (https://www.coinworld.com/news/world-coins/2017/08/royal-mint-error-2-coin-confirmed-decade-later.all.html) showcases a 2007 £2 that stands out as it has been authenticated and *attributed* by Chris Barker, Assistant Curator of the Royal Mint Museum, and that makes it a very "special error" as any doubt as to the legitimacy of the coin's pedigree is beyond reproach.

The aforementioned bi-metallic-*cum-mono*-metallic "error" coin is spectacular to look at as it completely contrasts the very idea of a *bi*-metallic coin, and I imagine this is why there was so much fanfare over its discovery.

Bearing the aforementioned "error" in mind, a different kind of bi-metallic-*cum-mono*-metallic "error" occurs when a blank for a different denomination, or country even—as the Royal Mint strikes for many different countries—finds its way into the striking chamber and you get a full cupro-nickel example as seen in **Image 4** and **Image 5**. These "Struck on Wrong Planchet/Foreign Planchet errors" are superb "errors" in their own right, with substantial eye appeal and as such, collectability, and are far more likely to occur—relatively speaking of course—than the aforementioned 2007 example where the "inner core" was never punched out . . . which

subsequently means the everyday collector has an opportunity to add one to their collection!

Image 4. 2008 £2 "Mono-metallic CuNi".

Image 5. £2 "Struck on a Wrong/Foreign Planchet".

In closing this discussion on bi-metallic "errors" that have surfaced or been catalogued to date, I would be amiss to not mention that many of the possible "errors" on the £2 have also been seen on the new 12-sided bi-metallic £1 coins as well. However, as the bi-metallic "error" is a relatively new thing, there's always the possibility of new unlisted examples surfacing and rest assured I will let you know if and when they do, through the pages of COIN NEWS! If you think you have a genuine Royal Mint error coin and would like it verified I would be happy to help. I can be contacted at the email address on page 31.

Something to ponder is that we are seeing a move towards *tri*-metallic coins by the world's mints, predominantly for "collector issues" it must be said, but speculation exists as to how long before a circulation coin consisting of three parts becomes a reality . . . and how long after that does a range of entirely new and unlisted *tri*-metallic "errors" make its way into circulation?

ONE POUND

The "round pound"

Specifications

Diameter	22.5mm
Weight	9.5g
Thickness	3.15mm
Composition	Nickel Brass (70% copper, 5.5% nickel, 24.5% zinc)
Edge	Milled with inscription/design

The original £1 coin was introduced in April 1983. It was made of nickel brass to give it a gold colour and was intentionally modelled (in size at least) on the gold sovereign which had been used as a £1 coin right up until World War I. Only the need to conserve gold during the war led to the introduction of a £1 note and by the 1980s it was decided it was time for a coin again. This was mainly down to cost, a £1 note simply didn't last as long as a coin and in the long run a coin was more economical.

The first £1 coin had the Royal Coat of Arms on it and used edge lettering for the very first time on a decimal coin, with the words DECUS ET TUTAMEN, which are Latin meaning *"An ornament and safeguard"*. The next year saw the design change to the Thistle of Scotland with the words NEMO ME IMPUNE LACESSIT (*no one touches me with impunity*) and in 1985 the Welsh Leek was used with the words PLEIDIOL WYF I'M GWLAD (*true I am to my country*). In 1986 the Flax, representing Northern Ireland (with Decus et Tutamen again) featured on the reverse of the coins and the following year saw the English Oak appear. Since then, right up until 2016, the design has changed every year—either to feature a representation of the UK as a whole (like the Coat of Arms or the Shield of Arms) or one of the four "home" countries.

Most often the designs have been heraldic (Lion of Scotland, Three Lions of England, Celtic Cross of Northern Ireland, Dragon of Wales, etc.) or floral (the Leek, Thistle, Flax, Oak, etc.). There were two other series issued: the Bridges series from 2004 to 2007 (featuring the Forth Rail Bridge for Scotland, the Menai Bridge for Wales, the Gateshead Millennium Bridge for England and the Egyptian Arch Bridge for Northern Ireland) and in 2010–11 there was the Cities series featuring London, Belfast, Cardiff and Edinburgh. The Edinburgh coin was the most sought after of these, indeed the most sought after of all £1 coins, as it had a relatively small mintage of under 1,000,000.

In 2015 it was announced that the "round pound" was to be scrapped—apparently 1 in 30 of them in circulation was a forgery (often simply lead painted gold) and the Royal Mint needed to clamp down on this. A new 12-sided coin (based on the old pre-decimal 12-sided threepenny piece and with special anti-counterfeit measures on it) was announced and in 2016 the last round pound was issued featuring four heraldic beasts surrounding a crown.

On March 28, 2017, the first of the 12-sided £1 coins was issued and the two ran in tandem up until October 15 of that year when the old "round pound" lost its legal tender status. You can no longer spend the coins in shops but banks will still take them for their customers—we have included them here because we know people collect them and will want to know more about the coins they have.

There are no real rarities in the £1 coin series—the Edinburgh coin had the lowest mintage at 935,000 so was the scarcest (but it can't properly be called a "rare" coin) and the final designs (the 2015 heraldic arms and the 2016 beasts) simply weren't around long enough for everyone to be able to get one. However, don't be fooled into thinking that the 2015 design was a rare coin or even scarce, as there were over 129,000,000 minted! We don't have exact figures for the 2106 "last" design—partly because this could be minted by visitors to the "Royal Mint Experience" in South Wales (see pages 64–66) and no records of these are available, but it is unlikely to be considered rare.

British Coinage

1983, 1993, 1998,
2003, 2008
Royal Arms

1984, 1989
Scottish Thistle

1985, 1990
Welsh Leek

1986, 1991
Northern Ireland Flax

1987, 1992
English Oak

1988
Crowned Shield

1994, 1999
Scottish Lion

1995, 2000
Welsh Dragon

1996, 2001
Northern Ireland Celtic
Cross

1997, 2002
English Lions

2004
Forth Railway Bridge

2005
Menai Bridge

2006
Egyptian Arch

2007
Gateshead Millennium
Bridge

2008, 2009, 2010, 2011,
2012, 2013, 2014, 2015
Uncrowned Shield

£1

£1 coin collection 1983–2016

2010
London

2010
Belfast

2011
Cardiff

THE SCARCE ONE

2011
Edinburgh

2013
English Oak and Rose

2013
Welsh Leek and Daffodil

2014
Scottish Thistle and
Bluebell

2014
Northern Ireland Flax and
Shamrock

2015
Heraldic Royal Arms

2016
Last Round Pound

What's it worth?

DATE	Mintage	Value
1983 Royal Arms	443,053,510	£3
1984 Scottish Thistle	146,256,501	£3
1985 Welsh Leek	228,430,749	£3
1986 Northern Ireland Flax	10,409,501	£3
1987 English Oak	39,298,502	£3
1988 Crowned Shield	7,118,825	£4
1989 Scottish Thistle	70,580,501	£4
1990 Welsh Leek	97,269,302	£4
1991 Northern Ireland Flax	38,443,575	£3
1992 English Oak	36,320,487	£2
1993 Royal Arms	114,744,500	£3
1994 Scottish Lion	29,752,525	£4
1995 Welsh Dragon	34,503,501	£3
1996 Northern Ireland Celtic Cross	89,886,000	£4
1997 English Lions	57,117,450	£4
1998 Royal Arms	Unknown	£15
1999 Scottish Lion	Unknown	£15
2000 Welsh Dragon	109,496,500	£3
2001 Northern Ireland Celtic Cross	63,968,065	£3
2002 English Lions	77,818,000	£3
2003 Royal Arms	61,596,500	£4
2004 Forth Railway Bridge	39,162,000	£4
2005 Menai Bridge	99,429,500	£4
2006 Egyptian Arch	38,938,000	£4
2007 Gateshead Millennium Bridge	26,180,160	£4
2008 Royal Arms	3,910,000	£3
2008 Uncrowned Shield	43,827,300	£3
2009 Uncrowned Shield	27,625,600	£2
2010 Uncrowned Shield	57,120,000	£2
2010 City Series (London)	2,635,000	£3
2010 City Series (Belfast)	6,205,000	£2
2011 Uncrowned Shield	25,415,000	£2
2011 City Series (Cardiff)	1,615,000	£5
2011 City Series (Edinburgh)	935,000	£6
2012 Uncrowned Shield	35,700,030	£2
2013 Uncrowned Shield	13,090,500	£2
2013 Floral Series (England)	5,270,000	£2
2013 Floral Series (Wales)	5,270,000	£2
2014 Uncrowned Shield	79,305,200	£2
2014 Floral Series (Scotland)	5,185,000	£2
2014 Floral Series (Northern Ireland)	5,780,000	£2
2015 Uncrowned Shield	29,580,000	£3
2015 Uncrowned Shield with *New Portrait* on obverse	62,495,640	£3
2015 Heraldic Royal Arms 5th	129,616,985	£3
2016 Uncrowned Shield	—	£20
2016 The Last Round Pound with representations of the beasts of England, Scotland, Wales and Northern Ireland	Unknown	£15

NOTE: Many of the more expensive £1 coins were only issued in Year Sets.

1983, 1993, 1998, 2003, 2008
The Royal Arms

1988
Crowned shield

2008 onwards
Uncrowned shield

Forgeries—BEWARE

If you are collecting round pounds be sure you don't have a fake in your collection—fakes will generally look a bit odd (have the wrong colour, maybe they will look a bit too worn where they haven't been struck properly) and they will often have the heads and tails sides not lining up (when you hold the coin with the Queen upright the "tails" side should be upright too. The easiest way to spot a fake is to look if the design corresponds with the date and to check the edge inscription; the forgers often didn't bother to match the right date to the right design or the right design to the correct inscription so you might end up with a 1983 Menai Bridge (it should be the Coat of Arms) or a 2002 Dragon (it should be the three lions) or maybe you have a Welsh Leek design with a Scottish inscription or an English three lions with Welsh edge lettering. You can check yours against our guide to make sure you only have genuine coins!

ONE POUND

The new 12-sided coin

Specifications

Diameter	23.03mm
Weight	8.75g
Thickness	2.80mm
Composition	Outer ring: Nickel-brass
	Centre: Nickel plated alloy
Edge	Milled on alternate sections

The old "round pound" was introduced in 1983 and since then it had become the most counterfeited British coin ever, with the Treasury estimating that 1 in 33 (some reports put the figure as high as 1 in 20) were fake—that's a total of over £50,000,000! This clearly couldn't go on and in 2015 the Royal Mint announced that there was to be a new £1 with special anti-counterfeiting features in place to make the forging of the coins virtually impossible.

As the 12-sided £1 is still relatively new there are few varieties worth more than face value. Most are concerned with the positioning of the two metals and the striking of the design on each. There's certainly no truth in the myth that those dated 2016 are worth more. Because of the sheer numbers needed many were minted in advance and given the date 2016. There are millions of them out there so don't be fooled! One variety is the coin with a special mintmark found issued in a pair with the last round pound. There are also reports of errors turning up, including the well-known "Leftie" which has a *milled* edge to the left of the obverse hologram; another has 2016 date with 2017 micro-lettering! But it seems that many apparently faulty coins are created after minting by unscrupulous individuals trying to make a profit. So be careful!

LOOK OUT!

Think you've got an error?

Most of us will have lurking in our collections an error coin, or what we may think is an error coin, however, if you are not quite sure whether it is a man-made error or a legitimate mint error then Scott Wren, who regularly writes for COIN NEWS, is making available his 20-plus years of experience specialising in errors and varieties by offering a free error identification and attribution service for readers. All you have to do is simply send as much detail as possible, along with clear images, to scoby01@hotmail.com and Scott will endeavour to establish if the coin is a legitimate mint error, and if it is, he will advise you of its official designation or attribution. This free service is being made available to assist the UK numismatic community to negotiate this often murky area of numismatics. The benefit of this free service is that after receiving the free attribution, your error coin can be submitted to the Royal Mint Authentication & Valuation Service safe in the knowledge that it is unlikely to be returned as "non-genuine/Post Mint Damage (PMD)", thereby saving any unnecessary time and money.

Fun fact

The micro-lettering below the rim should read ONE POUND on one side and the date of the coin on the other, but a few have been spotted showing different dates—these are worth looking out for so keep your magnifier handy!

What's it worth?

DATE	Mintage	Value
2016 Nations of the Crown	648,936,536	£2
2016 — With special cross crosslet mintmark (issued in special pack with a last round pound)	10,000	£55
2016 with micro-lettering reading 2017	Unknown	£75
2017 Nations of the Crown	749,616,200	£1
2018 Nations of the Crown	—	£1
2019 Nations of the Crown	—	£1
All "Lefties" are worth a small premium		

A NOTE ON TRIAL PIECES

TRIAL PIECE

Prior to the introduction of the new £1 coin into general circulation a number of trial pieces were issued to allow retailers, electronics manufacturers and other interested parties to test the new coin. These trial pieces are dated 2015 and feature Her Majesty's portrait on the obverse with the Royal Mint logo and the words "Trial Piece" on the reverse. These coins are not legal tender and were supposed to be returned to the Royal Mint once testing was over. However, as is so often the way, the request to return the pieces was missed by some and so a few of the coins made their way to online auction sites where they started to fetch £200 or thereabouts. They should not actually have been listed at all. They remain the property of the Royal Mint and should all have been returned and now if the Royal Mint is alerted to such a piece being offered on the open market they have said they will take action to retrieve it. Our advice is if you see a 12-sided £1 trial piece for sale don't buy it—it is officially Royal Mint property, you shouldn't have it, you could find it difficult to sell on and may find that you end up seriously out of pocket if you have to give it up. It is possible that the Mint will make these trial pieces available in collectors' packs (they did in 1994 with a bi-metallic £2 coin trial pack) but until they do, steer clear—you have been warned!

DID YOU KNOW?

THAT the winner of the open competition to design the 12-sided one pound coin was a 15-year-old schoolboy?

The winning design, chosen from literally hundreds of entries, was the one by Walsall student David Pearce and the person who informed him that he had won and his design was to be used for the circulating coinage was the then Chancellor of the Exchequer, George Osborne who, because of his position, was also the Master of the Royal Mint. David told us that the first he heard of his success was a telephone call from Mr Osborne in person! David (right) was later invited to 10 Downing Street to meet the Chancellor and to see the first striking of his design on a coin.

THE FIFTY PENCES

OFFSIDE EXPLAINED

OFFSIDE □ △NOT OFFSIDE

50 PENCE

RARE 50p

FIFTY PENCE

50 PENCE

BEATRIX POTTER 1866 1948

FIFTY PENCE

The first seven-sided coin

Specifications

Diameter	27.3mm since 1997
Weight	8.0g
Thickness	1.78mm
Composition	Cupro-nickel
	(75% copper, 25% nickel)
Edge	Plain

The fifty pence (50p) coin was first introduced in 1968 in preparation for the country's change to decimalisation. It replaced the ten shilling (10/-) note that had been in circulation in one form or another since World War I when it was introduced as a replacement for the half sovereign at a time when the Bank of England wanted to reduce the amount of gold in circulation. The 50p was the very first heptagonal (seven-sided) British coin although the public were used to non-round coins as they had been using a 12-sided three pence piece for some time.

At 30mm the original 50p was larger than the one we use today, as in 1997 a new smaller coin was brought in (in line with the smaller 5p and 10p that had been introduced a few years earlier). Since then it has had two main designs (Britannia up until 2008 and then lower part of the "Shield" series) as well as lots of other commemorative designs. Alongside the £2 it is the coin that is primarily used to celebrate special occasions and anniversaries and in 2011 a series of 29 50p coins was issued ready for the 2012 Olympics.

The original larger 50p had also been used as a commemorative piece at times and whilst Britannia was the main design used for nearly thirty years, there was a special commemoration coin in 1973 showing nine hands in a circle to celebrate the United Kingdom's accession to the EEC (as the EU was called back then). Another coin was issued for 1992 and 1993 celebrating Britain's Presidency of the European Council (this time it was called the EC), which is scarce and another in 1994 to commemorate the 50th anniversary of the Normandy Landings and D-Day.

Since 1997 there have been numerous commemorative designs in addition to the 29

Olympic designs! Most of the 50p coins are minted in their millions but now and again there are smaller mintages and these are the coins to look out for. The one everyone is looking for is the Kew Gardens coin from 2009. Struck to commemorate the 250th anniversary of the foundation of the Botanical Gardens at Kew, only 210,000 were minted, making it the rarest 50p in circulation at the moment by far. Uncirculated examples are changing hands for over £100!

Apart from Kew Gardens the next "rarest" of the non-Olympic coins is the 2017 Sir Isaac Newton 50p of which there were only 1,800,000. Next comes the Jemima Puddleduck coin minted in 2016, there were 2.1 million of those. Then the 50th Anniversary of the World Wide Fund for Nature (WWF) in 2011 with 3.4 million pieces minted and then the Centenary of the Scout Movement coin in 2007 of which there were 3.5 million.

As you can see with numbers like this these coins cannot be considered rarities and whilst they may be scarcer than some of the others—for example there were 7.4 million of the Girl Guides Centenary coins issued in 2010 and 6.9 million of the 150th anniversary of the birth of Beatrix Potter (the one without any character on it). But that doesn't mean they are going to be worth any more than 50p, certainly not to a dealer if you come to sell. As always, those in Brilliant Uncirculated condition (never been touched) in their original packaging will fetch more, but a standard 50p from your purse or pocket won't make you rich.

You may be tempted to buy any of the coins that you are missing from on-line auctions sites for more than face value and that's OK if, (a) you can afford it and (b) you don't expect to get your money back when you come to sell!

British Coinage

50p coin collection 1969–1994

Standard reverse

Accesssion to
the EEC

Presidency of
the EC

Anniversary of
the Normandy
Landings

What's it worth?

Old (large, 30mm) size 50 pence

DATE	Mintage	Value
1969 Britannia	188,400,000	£2
1970 Britannia	19,461,500	£3
1973 Accession to EEC	89,775,000	£3
1976 Britannia	43,746,500	£2
1977 Britannia	49,536,000	£2
1978 Britannia	72,005,000	£2
1979 Britannia	58,680,000	£2
1980 Britannia	89,086,000	£2
1981 Britannia	74,002,000	£2
1982 Britannia	51,312,000	£3
1983 Britannia	62,824,000	£2
1984 Britannia	158,820	£5
1985 Britannia	682,103	£2
1992/93 Presidency of the European Council	109,000	£75
1994 50th Anniversary of the Normandy Landings	6,705,520	£3

Fun fact

The reverse of the standard 50p coin carried the words NEW PENCE up to 1982 when the wording changed to FIFTY PENCE

50p coin collection 1997–2019

What's it worth?

DATE	Mintage	Value
1997 Britannia	456,364,100	£2
1998 Britannia	64,306,500	£2
1998 Presidency and		
25th Anniversary of EU entry	5,043,000	£3
1998 50th Anniversary of the		
National Health Service	5,001,000	£3
1999 Britannia	24,905,000	£2
2000 Britannia	27,915,500	£2
2000 150th Anniversary of		
Public Libraries	11,263,000	£2
2001 Britannia	84,998,500	£2
2002 Britannia	23,907,500	£2
2003 Britannia	23,583,000	£2
2003 Centenary of the Suffragette		
Movement	3,124,030	£4
2004 Britannia	35,315,500	£2
2004 Anniversary of Roger Bannister's		
4-minute mile	9,032,500	£3
2005 Britannia	25,363,500	£2
2005 250th Anniversary of Samuel Johnson		
and the Dictionary	17,649,000	£3
2006 Britannia	24,567,000	£2
2006 Anniversary of the Victoria Cross,		
Heroic Acts	10,000,500	£3
The Award	12,087,000	£3
2007 Britannia	11,200,000	£2
2007 Centenary of the Scout		
Movement	7,710,750	£3
2008 Britannia	3,500,000	£2

The current size 50p

Britannia—
This is the reverse of the 50p from 1997 to 2008

1998
European Union

1998
National Health Service

2000
Public Libraries Act

2003
Suffragette Movement

2004
Four-minute Mile

2005
Johnson's Dictionary

2006
Victoria Cross *Heroic Acts*

2007
Victoria Cross *The Medal*

2007
Scout Movement

50p coin collection 1997–2019

The current Shield design was introduced in 2008

2009 Kew Gardens—
THE RARE ONE

What's it worth?

DATE	Mintage	Value
2008 *New Shield Reverse*	22,747,000	£5
2009 Shield (in sets only)	106,332	£10
2009 250th Anniversary of Kew Gardens	**210,000**	**£100+**
2010 Shield (in sets only)	69,189	£15
2010 Centenary of Girl Guiding UK	7,410,090	£3
2011 50th Anniversary of the WWF	3,400,000	£3
2011 Shield (in sets only)	56,007	£10
2012 Shield	32,300,030	£2 ✓
2013 Shield	10,301,000	£2
2013 Royal arms commemorating Christopher Ironside	7,000,000	£8 ✓
2013 Centenary of the Birth of Benjamin Britten	5,300,000	£8
2014 Shield	49,001,000	£2
2014 XXth Commonwealth Games	6,500,000	£8
2015 Shield	20,101,000	£2 ✓
2015 75th Anniversary of the Battle of Britain	5,900,00	£4*

* Coins with no denomination in the obverse legend are from the Royal Mint Year Sets and are worth at least double.

DATE	Mintage	Value
2015 Shield *New Portrait*	39,300,00	£2
2016 950th Anniversary of the Battle of Hastings	6,700,000	£5
2016 Team GB for Rio Olympics	6,400,000	£3
2017 Shield	1,800,000	£4
2017 375th Anniversary of Sir Isaac Newton's birth	1,801,500	£5*

* "Strike your own" coins dated 2018 can fetch from £10 upwards

DATE	Mintage	Value
2018 Anniversary of the Representation of the People Act	—	£3

2010
Girl Guiding

2011
World Wildlife Fund

2013
Christopher Ironside

2013
Benjamin Britten

2014
Commonwealth Games

2015
Battle of Britain

2016
Battle of Hastings

2016
Team GB for Rio

2017
Sir Isaac Newton

2018
Representation of the People Act

British Coinage

50p coin collection 1997–2019

For 2019 no less than six different 50p coins have been struck, but only the Sherlock Holmes and the two Paddington coins have been issued for circulation—the other four are only available as limited edition BU coins in special presentation packs, as well as the usual collector versions. But remember these packs are often broken up, so watch out for them in your change!

2018
The Snowman

Stephen Hawking

The Gruffalo

Peter Rabbit

Sherlock Holmes

Paddington at
St. Paul's

Paddington at the
Tower of London

What's it worth?

DATE	Mintage	Value
2018 The Snowman	—	£10
2019 Stephen Hawking	—	£10
2019 The Gruffalo	—	£10
2019 Peter Rabbit	—	£10
2019 Sherlock Holmes	—	£3
2019 Paddington At St Paul's	—	£3
2019 Paddington at the Tower	—	£3

Commemorative Sets

Each year the Royal Mint produces sets containing examples of the coins issued for circulation. They also produce Proof sets of the same—these are coins which are struck to a higher standard than circulation coins. In addition some coins are only available individually or as part of a set in special illustrated presentation folders. Sometimes these sets and folders get broken up and the coins spent and thus enter into circulation. Should you be lucky enough to find a coin not listed in this book then you have probably come across one from a set or special issue.

The sets shown here are two of those produced for 2019, comprising coins that are not in general circulation. These include the rare Kew gardens 50p re-struck to celebrate 50 years of the 50p but it will be dated 2019 not 2009 as the original—will this be another rarity in time? For more details of Royal Mint issues visit their website: www.royalmint.com.

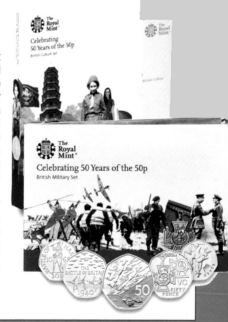

The Olympics 50p

In July 2007 it was announced that London would hold the 2012 Olympic Games, becoming the first city to host the Games three times (1908 and 1948 being the other two). In 2009 the Royal Mint announced a public competition to design the reverses for the planned Olympic 50p series and two years later the first winner, nine-year-old Florence Jackson, had her design unveiled on the BBC's *Blue Peter* programme (the programme had been asked to run the competition for their viewers and at age nine Florence became the youngest-ever designer of a British coin with her picture of a high-jumper). A special edition dated 2009 is now very rare.

In total 27 designers came up with 29 designs representing various Olympic and Paralympic sports. (It was a "blind" competition, meaning the Royal Mint didn't know who had designed what and two artists, Jonathon Olliffe and Natasha Ratcliffe, were lucky enough to have two of their designs chosen). It had been thought that the coins would be released in small batches, one or two designs at a time, but the logistics of this made it impossible and so in late 2011 all of the designs became available.

None of the standard Olympic coins are very rare but nor are they that common—with mintages ranging from 1,125,000 for the Football (Offside Rule) coin, up to 3,345,000 for the Archery 50p, every one is worth keeping if you find it, just for fun if nothing else. They are great to collect, however, there is a real rarity to look out for in this series!

When the coins were first issued they came in packs and were sold through W. H. Smith, the High Street newsagent. In those packs was the first striking of the Aquatics 50p, with the swimmer looking like she is underwater with wavy lines obscuring her face. When the coins were ready for general circulation those wavy lines had disappeared and the swimmer's face is clearly visible. Apparently it was felt the design looked better without the water obscuring the face and now the "underwater swimmer" coin has become a real collectable.

We don't know how many of this rare first type were issued but it won't be very many and now the coin is changing hands for almost £1,000! Although they were originally issued only in the special packs, it is perfectly possible that some have found their way into general circulation so it's definitely one to watch out for!

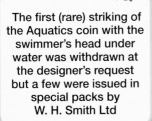

Rare find

The first (rare) striking of the Aquatics coin with the swimmer's head under water was withdrawn at the designer's request but a few were issued in special packs by W. H. Smith Ltd

What's it worth?

DATE	Mintage	Value
2011 Olympic & Paralympic Sports Issues:		
Aquatics		
— **Head with lines (under water)**	Unknown	**£850+**
— Head clear of lines	2,179,000	£4
Archery	3,345,000	£2
Athletics	2,224,000	£2
A special "Blue Peter" edition of this coin dated 2009 was also issued	19,751	£100
Badminton ✓	2,133,500	£2
Basketball	1,748,000	£2
Boccia	2,166,000	£2
Boxing	2,148,500	£2
Canoeing	2,166,500	£2
Cycling	2,090,500	£2
Equestrian	2,142,500	£2
Fencing	2,115,500	£2
Football	1,125,500	£10
Goalball	1,615,500	£10
Gymnastics	1,720,813	£2
Handball	1,676,500	£8
Hockey	1,773,500	£2
Judo	1,161,500	£10
Modern Pentathlon	1,689,500	£2
Rowing	1,717,300	£2
Sailing	1,749,500	£2
Shooting ✓	1,656,500	£2
Table Tennis	1,737,500	£2
Taekwondo	1,664,000	£2
Tennis	1,454,000	£8
Triathlon	1,163,500	£10
Volleyball	2,133,500	£2
Weightlifting	1,879,500	£2
Wheelchair Rugby	1,765,500	£2
Wrestling	1,129,500	£10

Head with lines (under water)

Head clear of lines

Other ones to look out for

50p coin collection 1997–2019

Aquatics
by Jonathan Olliffe

Archery
by Piotr Powaga

Athletics
by Florence Jackson

Badminton
by Emma Kelly

Basketball
by Sarah Payne

Boccia
by Justin Chung

Boxing
by Shane Abery

Canoeing
by Timothy Lees

Cycling
by Theo Crutchley-Mack

Equestrian
by Thomas Babbage

Fencing
by Ruth Summerfield

Football
by Neil Wolfson

British Coinage

50p coin collection 1997–2019

Goalball
by Jonathan Wren

Gymnastics
by Jonathan Olliffe

Handball
by Natasha Ratcliffe

Hockey
by Robert Evans

Judo
by David Cornell

Modern Pentathlon
by Daniel Brittain

Rowing
by Davey Podmore

Sailing
by Bruce Rushin

Shooting
by Pravin Dewdhory

Table Tennis
by Alan Linsdell

Taekwando
by David Gibbons

Tennis
by Tracy Baines

British Coinage

50p coin collection 1997–2019

Triathlon
by Sarah Harvey

Volleyball
by Daniela Boothman

Weight Lifting
by Rob Shakespeare

Wheelchair Rugby
by Natasha Ratcliffe

Wrestling
by Roderick Enriquez

Fun fact

A Paddington toy was the first item handed to the French workers by the British when the Channel Tunnel was finally linked in 1994.

Fun fact

Beatrix Potter's pet rabbit called Benjamin Bouncer was her inspiration for her famous book "The Tale of Peter Rabbit".

In 2016 The Royal Mint announced there was to be a series of 50p coins to celebrate the 150th anniversary of the birth of the children's author Beatrix Potter. The new coins were to be issued as circulating coins, in BU (brilliant uncirculated) packs and as silver and silver piedfort (double thickness) coins—with the silver examples having coloured highlights on the reverse. There were five coins issued at first, one featured a small cameo portrait of Miss Potter, her name and the dates 1866–1943 and a small image of Peter Rabbit at the bottom, but it is the later additions to the series that have really caught the public's attention as each one features a much loved Beatrix Potter character, with the design taken directly from Miss Potter's books.

The first to appear were Jemima Puddle-Duck, Mrs Tiggy-Winkle the hedgehog, Squirrel Nutkin and of course, Peter Rabbit. So popular were these coins that the Royal Mint issued four more in 2017—Peter Rabbit got a second appearance and now he was joined by Mr Jeremy Fisher the frog, Tom Kitten and Benjamin Bunny. 2018 saw another Peter Rabbit design (this time with carrots!) as well as coins for Flopsy Bunny, the Tailor of Gloucester (a helpful little mouse) and Mrs Tittlemouse. However, sadly, the 2019 Peter Rabbit coin portraying a three-quarter front facing Peter looking rather grumpy, is only available in the Royal Mint pack—until someone decides to spend theirs (as they sometimes do) and they enter circulation.

This series has proved amazingly popular, with people of all ages scouring their change for a Beatrix Potter coin—even though they were actually minted in reasonably large numbers. We don't have the figures for 2018 yet but we do know that the original 2016 Peter Rabbit had a mintage 9.7 million with the 2017 version over double that at 19.8 million. There were 5 million Squirrel Nutkin coins made, and 25 million Benjamin Bunnies were struck, the only halfway rare coin is Jemima Puddle-Duck with a figure of 2.1 million coins out there—but that's hardly scarce!

We know that these coins are making more than 50p on-line with people desperate to add that missing one to their collection and, as is always the case, that's fine if that is what you want to do—but please don't pay too much and remember when you come to sell the coin it probably won't be worth anywhere near what you paid for it—especially if the price was as high as some we've seen on auction sites! These coins are only "scarce" because there are lots of people collecting them, but that doesn't mean they aren't out there nor that you won't find one if you're patient—there are lots and lots in circulation, so please don't pay a vastly inflated price for one just because you can't wait!

Celebrating the 60th anniversary of his creation, Paddington Bear is another popular character we are now finding in our change. Two coins were issued in 2018 (Paddington at the station bearing his name and another at Buckingham Palace) and two more in 2019 (at the Tower of London and at St Paul's). Just like the Beatrix Potter coins the silver Paddingtons have coloured highlights but you won't find these in your change so they are not included in our listing. It is certainly possible that there may be more in the series, just as there may be more Beatrix Potter coins. There are host of other characters from the books that could keep this series running and running—long after the anniversary that they were originally struck to commemorate is a distant memory.

In 2018 the Snowman joined the list of characters and this year the Gruffalo, but neither will be found in your change as they are only available in special packs. It will be interesting to see what else the Royal Mint comes up with in the years to come.

Fun fact

Beatrix Potter was born in 1866 and was christened Helen after her Mother but was always known by her middle name Beatrix.

Bunnies, bears and other characters

2016
Beatrix Potter
150th Anniversary

2016
Peter Rabbit

2016 ✓
Mrs Tiggy-Winkle

2016
Squirrel Nutkin

2016
Jemima Puddle-Duck

2017
Tale of Peter Rabbit

2017
Jeremy Fisher

2017
Tom Kitten

2017
Benjamin Bunny

2018
Peter Rabbit

2018
Flopsy Bunny

2018
The Tailor of Gloucester

2018
Mrs. Tittlemouse

2018 ✓
Paddington Bear
at Paddington Station

2018
Paddington Bear
at Buckingham Palace

2018
The Snowman

2019
The Gruffalo

2019
Peter Rabbit

Paddington at the
Tower of London

Paddington at
St. Paul's

What's it worth?

DATE	MINTAGE	Value
Coins to celebrate the 150th Anniversary of Beatrix Potter		
2016 Peter Rabbit and the Author	6,900,000	£2
2016 Peter Rabbit	9,700,000	£4
2016 Jemima Puddle-Duck	2,100,000	£3
2016 Mrs. Tiggy-Winkle	8,800,000	£3 ✓
2016 Squirrel Nutkin	5,000,000	£3
2017 Peter Rabbit	19,900,000	£4 ✓
2017 Mr. Jeremy Fisher	9,900,000	£4
2017 Tom Kitten	9,500,000	£4
2017 Benjamin Bunny	25,000,000	£4
2018 Peter Rabbit	—	£5
2018 Flopsy Bunny	—	£5
2018 The Tailor of Gloucester	—	£5
2018 Mrs. Tittlemouse	—	£5
2019 Peter Rabbit	—	£10
Coins to celebrate the 60th Anniversary of Paddington Bear		
2018 Paddington Bear at Paddington Station	—	£5 ✓
2018 Paddington at Buckingham Palace	—	£5
2019 Paddington at the Tower of London	—	£10
2019 Paddington at St. Paul's Cathedral	—	£10 ✓
Other "Characters"		
2018 The Snowman	—	£10
2019 The Gruffalo	—	£10

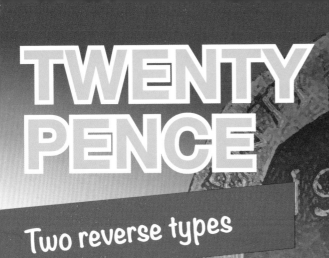

TWENTY PENCE

Two reverse types

Dated reverse
1982–2015

Undated reverse
2008–

Specifications

Diameter	21.4mm
Weight	5.0g
Thickness	1.7mm
Composition	Cupro-nickel (84% copper,16% nickel)
Edge	Plain

The 20p coin was introduced in 1982 and became Britain's second seven-sided coin after the 50p. Sticking with the heraldic theme common to other post-decimal British coins, the early 20p coin featured the Tudor Rose—first seen on crowns 500 years before.

None of these early 20p pieces are worth more than face value in anything other than uncirculated condition, although in 1986 no 20 pences were issued for circulation but those struck and issued in the annually-produced Royal Mint Year Sets are worth a small premium as are those dated 1992, the year that two different heads appeared on the coins, one very slightly larger than the other!

However, in 2008 the design was changed and the 20p, like the other coins of the realm, became part of the larger Shield of Arms design. This new design meant that the date was moved to the heads side of the coins, whereas on the original design it had featured on the tails side.

In early 2009 a caller to a BBC Radio Devon phone-in, where a member of the COIN NEWS team was taking calls on coins and banknotes, stated that she had one of the new 20 pences without a date on the front or the back. A visit to her home in Exeter proved the coin was genuine and very unusual! A week later a COIN NEWS reader sent in another example of this anomaly, this time from the Leeds area.

When the Royal Mint was approached about this issue it was discovered that a small batch of the new coins had been minted in error (probably 100,000-200,000, although no official figures are available), using the tails side of the new design but with the heads side of the old—meaning that the coin had no date at all! In numismatics this is known as a "mule" and this was the first time this had happened in hundreds of years (it was in 1551, in the reign of Edward VI, that dates first appeared on coins).

It is very rare for the Royal Mint to make such a glaring mistake and soon the coins were changing hands for over £100! The price has settled down somewhat in recent years as those who want the coin have got one and the market has therefore decreased but they are still worth around £40–50 even if you've pulled them from your purse or pocket—that's quite a return on 20p and as it is also a rare piece of numismatic history it is definitely something to look out for!

Fun fact

There are no less than five different "heads" on the circulating 20 pence coins, including the "modified" effigy used in late 1992 to replace the similar but smaller head used on the earlier pieces.

THE RARE FIND

Front (obverse)
No date shown

DATE		Mintage	Value
1982		740,815,000	50p
1983		158,463,000	50p
1984		65,350,000	50p
1985		74,273,699	50p
1986 (only issued in Year Sets)		167,000	£5
1987		137,450,000	50p
1988		38,038,344	50p
1989		132,013,890	50p
1990		88,097,500	50p
1991		35,901,250	50p
1992 Small head	Est. approx. 1,500,000*		£4
1992 Large head	Est. approx. 29,705,000*		£4
1993		123,123,750	50p
1994		67,131,250	50p
1995		102,005,000	50p
1996		83,163,750	50p
1997		89,518,750	50p
1998 *New portrait introduced*		76,965,000	50p
1999		73,478,750	50p
2000		136,428,750	50p
2001		148,122,500	50p
2002		93,360,000	50p
2003		153,383,750	50p
2004		120,212,500	50p
2005		124,488,750	50p
2006		114,800,000	50p
2007		117,075,000	50p
2008		11,900,000	50p
2008 *New reverse introduced, date now on obverse*		115,022,000	£2
2008 — paired with old obverse (thus no date)	Est. approx. 120,000 (?)		£65
2009		121,625,300	50p
2010		112,875,500	50p
2011		191,625,000	50p
2012		69,650,030	50p
2013		66,325,000	50p
2014		173,775,000	50p
2015		63,175,000	50p
2015 *New portrait introduced*		131,250,000	50p
2016		212,625,000	50p
2017		unknown	50p

*In 1992 the portrait was slightly modified so there are two types this year.

Back (reverse)
No date shown

Fun fact

The undated 20p is really the only one in the series worth looking out for. It is rare as our circulating coins have all carried the date since the 17th century.

The Royal Mint® Experience

The Royal Mint Experience is the only place in the world where you can watch the United Kingdom's coins being made. Go behind the scenes to follow the journey of a coin from a blank to a bank in our 45-minute Guided Factory Experience.

On your visit you can:

- Lift a 400oz Gold Bar worth £400,000
- Strike your very own coin
- Wander through our interactive exhibition
- Discover process needed to make a coin

20 minutes from Cardiff, open 7 days a week all year round.
0333 241 2223 | **royalmint.com/experience** | **experience@royalmint.com**

 facebook.com/TheRoyalMintExperience
instagram.com/royalmintexperience
twitter.com/RoyalMintExp

 youtube.com/Royal Mint Experience
linkedin.com/the-royal-mint-experience
www.tripadvisor.co.uk

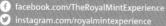

Winner of Visit Wales' gold quality assurance award

cpt coach friendly status

TEN PENCE

Specifications

Diameter	24.5mm
Weight	6.5g
Thickness	1.85mm
Composition	Nickel-plated steel (since January 2012)
	Cupro-nickel (prior to January 2012) (75% copper, 25% nickel)
Edge	Milled

Lions and Letters

Two different standard reverses exist in circulation for the 10 pence—the shield was introduced in 2008.

Like the 5p coin the 10p was introduced in 1968 as part of the changeover to decimal coinage planned for 1971. It was originally designed to be the same size and weight (28.5mm in diameter and 11.31g) as a coin already in use—the florin or two shilling piece. Both of these coins were in use in tandem as 10p coins right up until early 1993 when both were withdrawn in favour of a new, smaller and lighter (24.5mm and 6.5g) coin that had been introduced in September 1992.

The original, larger 10p coins and the first smaller ones had a crowned lion on the tails side but since the redesign of the coins in 2008 it now shows two of the three lions (sometimes called leopards in heraldry) of England that appear in the top left (or first quarter) of the "Shield of Arms". Like the 5p coin it was originally (both in large and small size) struck in cupro-nickel but since 2011 nickel plated steel has been used.

As millions of 10p coins are issued every year and because there have been neither major deviations from the two designs mentioned nor any errors, there hasn't been a large market for 10p coins amongst collectors up until recently and just about all would have been worth just face value. However, as you will read on the next page, things have recently begun to change.

NOTE:
The missing years were only issued as part of the Royal Mint Year Sets and are generally worth around £2 each.

What's it worth?

DATE	Mintage	Value
1968	336,143,250	25p
1969	314,008,000	25p
1970	133,571,000	25p
1971	63,205,000	25p
1973	152,174,000	25p
1974	92,741,000	25p
1975	181,559,000	25p
1976	228,220,000	25p
1977	59,323,000	50p
1979	115,457,000	50p
1980	88,650,000	50p
1981	3,487,000	£2
Size reduced		
1992	1,413,455,170	50p
1995	43,259,000	50p
1996	118,738,000	50p
1997	99,196,000	50p
New portrait		
2000	134,733,000	50p
2001	129,281,000	50p
2002	80,934,000	50p
2003	88,118,000	50p
2004	99,602,000	50p
2005	69,604,000	50p
2006	118,803,000	50p
2007	72,720,000	50p
2008	9,720,000	50p
New reverse		
2008	71,447,000	50p
2009	84,360,000	50p
2010	96,600,500	50p
2011	59,603,850	50p
2012	11,600,030	50p
2013	320,200,750	50p
2014	490,202,020	50p
2015	119,000,000	50p
New portrait		
2015	91,900,000	50p
2016	135,380,000	50p
2017	33,300,000	50p
2018	—	50p
2018 Alphabet series	—	from 50p
2019 Alphabet series	—	from 50p

In March 2018 The Royal Mint announced a major new design programme using 10 pence coins called The Great British Coin Hunt. The programme has seen 26 new designs released, each with a tails side showing a letter of the alphabet and a corresponding picture that represents a theme that is "quintessentially British" these designs are:

- A – Angel of the North
- B – Bond ... James Bond
- C – Cricket
- D – Double-decker bus
- E – English breakfast
- F – Fish and chips
- G – Greenwich Mean Time
- H – Houses of Parliament
- I – Ice cream
- J – Jubilee
- K – King Arthur
- L – Loch Ness
- M – Mackintosh
- N – NHS
- O – Oak tree
- P – Pillar box
- Q – Queuing
- R – Robin
- S – Stonehenge
- T – Tea
- U – Union Flag
- V – Village
- W – World Wide Web
- X – X marks the spot
- Y – Yeoman warder
- Z – Zebra crossing

Currently there is no indication of exactly how many of each of these coins have been issued nor where they will be found in the country—it could be that the same number of each is produced and they are put into banks the length and breadth of the land in equal batches, or it could be that some designs have smaller mintages than others and some are only to be found in one region and not others. How many there are and how they are distributed will have a huge effect on the value and our advice is to try and collect them all if you can—in a few years' time we will know exactly which, if any, are the rarities. In the meantime see how many you can find.

Most of the designs are now appearing on on-line auction sites and are being bid up to round about £1–2 with "Buy it Now" options at around the same price. The uncirculated packs are, as you would expect, going for more but none seem to be attracting big money—the premiums you do find will be created by those people willing to pay more for a coin they just haven't been able to find in their change, that doesn't mean that every coin with that letter on will be worth that nor that if you buy one at an inflated price you will be able to sell it for the same money in the future. With the 10p coins, as with series like the Olympic 50p coins the fun should be in the collecting rather than trying to make a profit. By all means pay a little bit over face value for one you just cannot find, but don't fall into the trap of thinking that means it will be worth a fortune later on!

The 2 shillings or florin, which was its old name, was replaced by the 10 pence in 1968 but it remained in circulation because it was the same size and had the same value as the 10p.

10p tips

There were two larger sizes of 10 pence (which replaced the florin or 2 shillings piece in 1968). Originally it read NEW PENCE and later TEN PENCE.

The size of the 10 pence was reduced in 1992 and the reverse design was changed in 2008.

Celebrating all things

BRITISH

A to Z—
the Great British coin hunt

Angel of the North

James Bond

Cricket

Double-decker bus

English breakfast

Fish and chips

Greenwich
Mean Time

Houses of
Parliament

Ice cream

Jubilee

King Arthur

Loch Ness

Mackintosh

NHS

Oak tree

Pillar box

Queueing

Robin

Stonehenge

Tea

Union Flag

Village

World Wide Web

X marks the spot

Yeoman warder

Zebra crossing

FIVE PENCE

The coin at the centre of the shield

There are two different reverses for the 5 pence in circulation—the shield was introduced in 2008.

Specifications

Diameter	18.0mm (from 1990)
Weight	3.25g
Thickness	1.7mm
Composition	Nickel-plated steel (since January 2012)
	Cupro-nickel (prior to January 2012) (75% copper, 25% nickel)
Edge	Milled

The 5p coin was first introduced in 1968 as part of the changeover to decimal coins. Old shillings were used alongside the "new pence" coins for a few years and the size and weight of the original 5p was designed to be the same as that of the shilling (23.59mm and 5.65g), which was useable in shops in exactly the same way as a "new" five pence coin. Over the next two decades the shillings were phased out and more and more five pence pieces were introduced. In December 1990 both the shillings and the original, shilling size, 5p coins were withdrawn and replaced by the smaller size 5p (18mm and 3.25g) that had been introduced in June of that year.

Fun fact

The first decimal five pence (5p) coins, issued in 1968, were the same size as the old one shilling (1/–) coin so they both circulated at the same time until they were both formally demonetised in 1990 and the 5p made smaller.

The small size one is the one we use today. It kept the same design as the original 5p (the Scottish thistle) up until the redesign of the coinage in 2008 when it was the coin at the centre of the "Shield of Arms" design. Both the original larger 5p coins and the smaller lighter ones were originally minted in cupro-nickel but as of 2011 they have been minted using nickel plated steel—the post-2011 coins are a little bit thicker than the earlier ones, being 1.89mm rather than 1.7mm. 5p coins are always minted in the tens of millions if not hundreds of millions and there have been no rarities to look out for meaning that they are, generally, worth only face value, although those only originally issued in the Year Sets will cost more.

Fun fact

There were over 1.6 BILLION small 5p coins minted in 1990 to get ready for the changeover in size, making it the largest production run of any British decimal coin—probably the biggest production run of any British coin ever!

by Arnold Machin

by Raphael Maklouf

by Ian Rank-Broadley

by Jody Clark

In common with the rest of the UK coinage there have been four different effigies of Her Majesty the Queen on the obverse (heads) side of the 5 pence coins.

What's it worth?

DATE	Mintage	Value
1968	98,868,250	50p
1969	120,270,000	50p
1970	225,948,525	50p
1971	81,783,475	50p
1975	141,539,000	50p
1977	24,308,000	50p
1978	61,094,000	50p
1979	155,456,000	50p
1980	220,566,000	50p
New Portrait introduced		
1987	48,220,000	50p
1988	120,744,610	50p
1989	101,406,000	50p
Size reduced		
1990	1,634,976,005	50p
1991	724,979,000	50p
1992	453,173,500	50p
1994	93,602,000	50p
1995	183,384,000	50p
1996	302,902,000	50p
1997	236,596,000	50p
New portrait introduced		
1998	217,376,000	50p
1999	195,490,000	50p
2000	388,512,000	50p
2001	337,930,000	50p
2002	219,258,000	50p
2003	333,230,000	50p
2004	271,810,000	50p
2005	236,212,000	50p
2006	317,697,000	50p
2007	246,720,000	50p
2008	92,880,000	50p
New reverse introduced		
2008	165,172,000	50p
2009	132,960,300	50p
2010	396,245,500	50p
2011	50,400,000	50p
2012	339,802,350	50p
2013	378,800,750	50p
2014	885,004,520	50p
2015	163,000,000	50p
New portrait introduced		
2015	536,600,000	50p
2016	305,740,000	50p
2017	220,515,000	50p

NOTE:
The missing years were only issued as part of the Royal Mint Year Sets and are generally worth around £2 each.

Learn more about the iconic SOVEREIGN

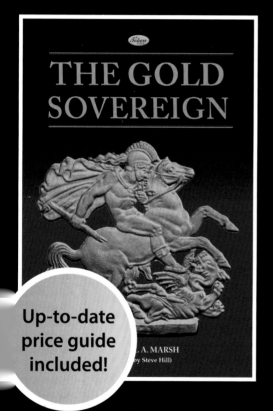

THE GOLD SOVEREIGN

Up-to-date price guide included!

L. A. MARSH
(by Steve Hill)

Michael Marsh's renowned work on the gold sovereign and half sovereign has been completely revised and updated for today's collector.

Michael Marsh's works on the sovereign and half sovereign need little introduction to most collectors. For years they have been the standard reference works on Britain's most revered gold coins and the Marsh numbers are used across the hobby by collectors, dealers and auction houses alike. Since the last editions of The Gold Sovereign and The Gold Half Sovereign there have been a number of additions to the series as well as a great deal of new information that has come to light.

Token Publishing Ltd recently bought the rights to republish the Marsh books and, after extensive revisions by Steve Hill of Sovereign Rarities (erstwhile of Spink and Baldwins), the new volume, incorporating the sovereign, half sovereign and new quarter sovereign is now available. This long-awaited new work is available to order priced at £35 (+ p&p) along with an accompanying price and rarity guide.

This hard-bound publication is set to become *the* reference work on this iconic coin.

Visit www.tokenpublishing.com
or telephone 01404 46972

TWO PENCE

The rarest Mule

There are three different reverses for the 2 pence (including the NEW PENCE type)—the shield was introduced in 2008.

Specifications

Diameter	25.9mm
Weight	7.12g
Thickness	Bronze: 1.85mm
	Copper-plated steel: 2.03mm
Composition	Bronze until September 1992 (97% copper, 2.5% zinc, 0.5% tin) Copper-plated steel since September 1992, except in 1998 when it was made in both alloys
Edge	Plain

A coin worth two pence was first introduced in the reign of Edward III (1327–77) but back then it was known as a half groat. The coin wasn't really called a "two pence" until 300 years later in the reign of Charles II when it was specially struck for the Maundy ceremony and not really used for general circulation. It was originally struck in silver, as were pennies, but in 1797 copper versions were produced for the first time—they were huge and were known as "cartwheels" because of their size. They were not popular coins (they were simply too big to be practical—it was 41mm or 1.6 inches in diameter and weighed 56.7g or 2oz!) and so the two penny coin vanished from circulation until 1971 when it was reintroduced following decimalisation and is still in use today.

When the coins were first introduced they, like all the new decimal coins, had the words NEW PENCE on the reverse (tails side). In 1982 this was replaced by the denomination—so NEW PENCE became FIVE PENCE, TEN PENCE, TWO PENCE etc. However, the following year it seems there was a mix up in production and the wrong reverse dies were used for a very limited time creating what is known as a "mule" (the head of one thing, the tail of another). A small number of 2p coins dated 1983 on the obverse (heads) side ended up with the tails side that said NEW PENCE not TWO PENCE as they should have done. We don't know exactly how many coins are in that small batch minted in error, but we do know the coins are worth a small fortune and can change hands for around £1,000!

Remember though, just because a coin has NEW PENCE on it doesn't make it valuable (they all did for ten years) and just because it is dated 1983, that doesn't make it valuable either. But put the two together and find a coin dated 1983 with NEW PENCE on it and you're in the money!

Fun fact

2p coins minted between 1971 and 1992 were all made from bronze—since then they have been struck in copper-plated steel. However, in 1998 and 1999, some were minted in bronze. The only way to tell them apart is to use a magnet!

THE RARE FIND

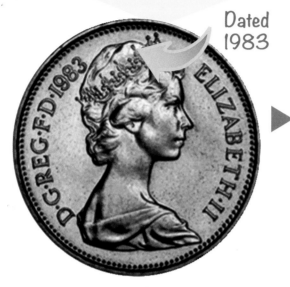

Dated 1983

The word "NEW" instead of "TWO"

What's it worth?

DATE	Mintage	Value
1971	1,454,856,250	50p
1975	145,545,000	50p
1976	181,379,000	50p
1977	109,281,000	50p
1978	189,658,000	£2
1979	260,200,000	50p
1980	408,527,000	50p
1981	353,191,000	50p
Legend changed to TWO PENCE		
1982	205,000	£2
1983	631,000	£2
1983 Error NEW instead of TWO	**—**	**£850+**
1984	158,820	£3
New portrait introduced		
1985	107,113,000	50p
1986	168,967,500	50p
1987	218,100,750	50p
1988	419,889,000	50p
1989	359,226,000	50p
1990	204,499,700	50p
1991	86,625,250	50p
1992 *Copper plated steel*	102,247,000	50p
1992 *Bronze*	Unknown	50p
1993	235,674,000	50p
1994	531,628,000	50p
1995	124,482,000	50p
1996	296,278,000	50p
1997	496,116,000	50p
New portrait introduced		
1998	115,154,000	50p
1998 *Bronze*	98,676,000	50p
1999	353,816,000	50p
2000	536,659,000	50p
2001	551,880,000	50p
2002	168,556,000	50p
2003	260,225,000	50p
2004	356,396,000	50p
2005	280,396,000	50p
2006	170,637,000	50p
2007	254,500,000	50p
2008	10,600,000	50p
New Reverse introduced		
2008	241,679,000	50p
2009	150,500,500	50p
2010	99,600,000	50p
2011	144,300,000	50p
2012	67,800,000	50p
2013	40,600,000	50p
2014	247,600,020	50p
2015	85,900,000	50p
New Portrait introduced		
2015	139,200,000	50p
2016	185,600,000	50p
2017	16,600,000	50p

NOTE: 1982, 1983 and 1984 were only issued as part of the Royal Mint Year Sets and are generally worth around £2 each.

ONE PENNY

Where it all began

Fun fact

Fun fact

The very first pennies were struck in the 8th century and were almost the same size as those issued today, but they were made of silver!

The penny has two reverse designs

The penny has been the central coin in the British Isles for over 1,000 years. Based on the Roman denarius the Penny was first introduced by King Offa of Mercia in the 8th century and was the only coin in use for the next 500 years until Edward I introduced other denominations like the groat (four pence) and the half penny.

Early pennies are collectable and some valuable but the most valuable are certain ones from the 20th century. Sadly you aren't likely to find them in your change though! In 1933 less than ten pennies were minted (probably only seven but there are no official records) and in 1954 there were officially no pennies at all but one is known to exist. These would be worth tens of thousands of pounds if they came up for sale today. Since decimalisation in 1971 there have been no pennies that are worth more than face value in circulated condition—there are simply too many of them minted for them to be valuable and, to our knowledge there have been no errors to look out for. For the very first time since 1972 the Royal Mint did not strike any pennies for circulation in 2018 or 2019.

Fun fact

In 1797 the penny was made of copper and contained 1 penny-worth of metal—which meant that it was HUGE at 36mm diameter and 5mm thick! They soon became known as "Cartwheels" and were very unpopular. They only circulated for 9 years until they were replaced by a smaller one in 1806.

Specifications

Diameter	20.3mm
Weight	3.56g
Thickness	Bronze: 1.52mm
	Copper-plated steel: 1.65mm
Composition	Bronze until September 1992
	(97% copper, 2.5% zinc, 0.5% tin)
	Copper-plated steel since
	September 1992
Edge	Plain

A hoard of silver pennies dating back to 1280 were found in a field in Lincolnshire in 2016.

Enlarged

Actual size

Penny of King Offa of Mercia (AD 757–796).

Penny of King George III (1760–1820) shown actual size.

Penny in copper of Queen Victoria (1837–1901) shown actual size.

Penny in bronze of King George VI (1936–1952) shown actual size.

As you can see above, since King Offa's time, the penny has undergone a number of changes to get to the size it is today!

What's it worth?

DATE		Mintage	Value
1971		1,521,666,250	10p
1973		280,196,000	20p
1974		330,892,000	20p
1975		221,604,000	20p
1976		300,160,000	20p
1977		285,430,000	20p
1978		292,770,000	20p
1979		459,000,000	20p
1980		416,304,000	20p
1981		301,800,000	20p
Legend changed to ONE PENNY			
1982		100,292,000	20p
1983		243,002,000	20p
1984		154,759,625	20p
New portrait introduced			
1985		200,605,245	20p
1986		369,989,130	20p
1987		499,946,000	20p
1988		793,492,000	20p
1989		658,142,000	20p
1990		529,047,500	20p
1991		206,457,600	20p
1992	*Copper-plated steel*	253,867,000	20p
1992	*Bronze*	78,421	£3
1993		602,590,000	20p
1994		843,834,000	20p
1995		303,314,000	20p
1996		723,840,060	20p
1997		396,874,000	20p
New portrait introduced			
1998		739,770,000	20p
1999		891,392,000	20p
2000		1,060,420,000	20p
2001		928,698,000	20p
2002		601,446,000	20p
2003		539,436,000	20p
2004		739,764,000	20p
2005		536,318,000	20p
2006		524,605,000	20p
2007		548,002,000	20p
2008		180,600,000	20p
New reverse introduced			
2008		507,952,000	20p
2009		556,412,800	20p
2010		609,603,000	20p
2011		431,004,000	20p
2012		227,201,000	20p
2013		260,800,000	20p
2014		464,801,520	20p
2015		154,600,000	20p
New portrait introduced			
2015		418,201,016	20p
2016		368,482,000	20p
2017		240,990,000	20p

HALF PENNY

The forgotten decimal coin

The halfpenny or "ha'penny" was first introduced by King Edward I in the late 13th century and remained a part of British coinage for centuries, first struck in silver and later in copper or bronze. From the reign of Charles II onwards the reverse showed an effigy of Britannia until it was changed to a ship (Francis Drake's Golden Hind) in 1937 at the beginning of the reign of George VI and continued right up to decimalisation. Even today there are thousands of these popular ship reverse halfpences around although they are worth very little.

Unlike many other coins (the farthing, the threepence, the sixpence, the shilling, the florin and the halfcrown) it survived decimalisation in 1971 in a much smaller size, but couldn't survive in the face of inflation as its buying power became less and less. It was in use right up until 1984 when minting of it was discontinued and it was demonetised in December of that year. Circulated examples are worth virtually nothing as millions of them were produced but a good uncirculated or proof example will be worth many times face value—unfortunately many times half a penny still isn't very much! However, it's the very last one that is worth a premium and worth searching for.

Specifications

Diameter	17.14mm
Weight	1.78g
Thickness	1mm
Composition	Bronze
Edge	Plain

What's it worth?

DATE	Mintage	Value
1971	1,394,188,250	20p
1973	365,680,000	20p
1974	365,448,000	20p
1975	197,600,000	20p
1976	412,172,000	20p
1977	66,368,000	20p
1978	59,532,000	20p
1979	219,1322,000	20p
1980	202,788,000	20p
1981	46,748,000	20p
1982 Legend changed from NEW PENNY to HALF PENNY	190,752,000	20p
1983	7,600,000	50p
1984 (the last one ever, only found as Proof in Year Sets)	40,000	£2

Fun fact

There are probably more old pre-decimal halfpences hiding in jars and containers than any other denomination. In the hope of making money when decimalisation happened millions of them were squirrelled away.

THE ROYAL MINT EXPERIENCE

SINCE the Royal Mint Experience opened in 2016 visitors have been flocking to the purpose-built visitors' centre at the Royal Mint's HQ at Llantrisant. The Experience offers a grand day out for all the family where the work and issues of one of the oldest mints in the world can be explored. To give you a taste of what awaits you on your visit, take a tour with us and explore the Royal Mint Experience . . .

The Royal Mint Experience tour offers a unique chance to see "behind the scenes" at the Royal Mint. See how our coins are made in the Royal Mint's processing plant—where blank discs of metal are transformed into the coins we all love to collect.

Exploring coins through the ages . . .

Coins have played a part in popular arcade games over the year—who remembers playing on one of these?

One of the amazing interactives allows visitors to explore three of the Royal Mint's homes—the Tower of London, Tower Hill in London and its newest one, the 35-acre site at Llantrisant in South Wales.

Visitors can watch a film showing the "journey of a coin" from the furnace through blanks to the actual striking.

AND FINALLY ...

At the end of an exciting and informative visit, where best to end your day, and spend some of the coins that you have just learned so much about, than a refreshing pit stop in the cafe and a visit to the Royal Mint Experience shop where you can purchase a memento of your day.

At the shop, for collectors of the A-Z 10 pences, there is a chance to swap your normal "shield" 10p for one of those elusive "Great British Coin Hunt" 10 pences and fill those pesky gaps in your collection!

All in all, a great day out awaits for you at the Royal Mint Experience. Remember to plan your visit by going online or telephoning the Royal Mint Experience and book your place on the a tour before setting off on a long journey—details appear below.

On the Royal Mint Experience tour you will learn more about the manufacturing process that goes into creating the coins in your pocket. As part of your tour, you will have the opportunity to strike your very own coin (the design of the coin alters, depending on what theme the Royal Mint are celebrating at the time of your visit—for instance, a popular "Strike your own" last year was the 2018-dated Sir Isaac Newton 50p coin). From June this year, visitors can strike their very own Sherlock Holmes 50p coin for a limited time. The opportunity is limited to one coin per person and can be purchased at check-in for £6.90 or pre-booked on-line. Pre-booking your tour is advisable—see the panel below for booking details.

PLAN YOUR VISIT

The Royal Mint is located 4 miles from Junction 34 of the M4. Drive past the main entrance to the Mint. The visitors' car park for The Royal Mint Experience is on the left opposite the Three Saints Hotel. The guided tour lasts 45 minutes, but allow a good couple of hours to explore the exhibits in the final exhibition hall. There are plenty of interactive exhibits to keep the children amused. There is a large cafeteria for visitors and a well-stocked shop selling souvenirs as well as coins.

Admission Prices:	Door £	Online £
Adult (16+)	13.50	13.00
Child (5-15 years)	11.00	10.50
Child under 5 years	Free	Free
Senior Citizens	12.00	11.50
Students	12.00	11.50
Family (1 adult/3 children Or 2 adults/2 children)	40.00	38.50

There are restrictions on the number of wheelchair users in any one group. Wheelchair users, or others with special needs, should telephone 0333 241 2223. This number can also be used to book a tour. The tours run at regular intervals throughout the day from 10am to 4.30pm. Remember all children under 16 must be accompanied by an adult at all times.

The Royal Mint Experience is open daily from 9.30am to 6.30pm except December 25 and 26 and January 1.

To plan your visit to the Royal Mint Experience go online at www.royalmint.com.

Images courtesy of the Royal Mint.

COIN CHECK LIST

Here you can mark off your coins as you find them. The list includes coins you should find in your change, but also listed are the older coins some of which were originally only included in Royal Mint Year Sets but over the years many have escaped into circulation. Also listed for completeness are the old larger size 50, 10 and 5 pence coins which turn up from time to time.

TWO POUNDS (£2)

1986 Commonwealth Games ✗ 6
1989 Tercentenary of Bill of Rights
1989 Tercentenary of Claim of Right
1994 Tercentenary of the Bank of England
1995 50th Anniversary of End of WWII
1995 50th Anniversary of the United Nations
1996 European Football Championships
1997 Standard design
1998 Standard design
1999 Standard design
1999 Rugby World Cup
2000 Standard design
2001 Standard design
2001 Marconi
2002 Standard design
2002 Commonwealth Games
    — Scotland
    — Wales
    — Northern Ireland
    — England
2003 Standard design
2003 DNA Double Helix
2004 Standard design
2004 Trevithick Steam Locomotive
2005 Standard design
2005 Gunpowder Plot
2005 End of World War II
2006 Standard design
2006 Brunel, The Man (Portrait)
2006 Brunel, His Achievements
    (Paddington Station)
2007 Standard design
2007 Tercentenary of the Act of Union
2007 Bicentenary of the Abolition
    of the Slave Trade
2008 Standard design
2008 Centenary of 4th Olympiad, London
2008 Olympic Games Handover from Beijing
2009 Standard design
2009 250th Anniversary of birth of Robert Burns
2009 200th Anniversary of birth of Charles
    Darwin

☑ 2010 Standard design ☑
☐ 2010 Florence Nightingale 150 Years of Nursing ☐
☐ 2011 Standard design ☐
☐ 2011 500th Anniversary of the Mary Rose ☐
☐ 2011 400th Anniversary of the King James Bible ☐
☐ 2012 Standard design ☐
☐ 2012 200th Anniversary of birth of Charles
    Dickens ☐
☑ 2012 Olympic Games Handover to Rio ☐
☐ 2013 Standard design ☐
    2013 150th Anniversary of the London Underground
☐   — Roundel design ☑
☐   — Train design ☐
☐ 2013 350th Anniversary of the Guinea ☑
☐ 2014 Standard design ☑
    2014 100th Anniversary of the Outbreak of WWI ☑
☐ 2014 500th Anniversary of Trinity House ☑
☐ 2015 Standard design ☑
☐ 2015 Anniversary of WWI — Royal Navy ☐
☐ 2015 800th Anniversary of Magna Carta ☐
☐ 2015 New Britannia standard design ☐
☑ 2016 Standard Britannia design ☐
☐ 2016 400th Anniversary of Shakespeare's death
☐   — Comedies ☐
☐   — Tragedies ☐
☑   — Histories ☑
☑ 2016 350th Anniversary of the Great Fire
☐   of London ☐
☑ 2016 Anniversary of WWI — Army ☐
    2017 Anniversary of WWI — Aviation ☐
☐ 2017 Anniversary of Jane Austen ☐
☐ 2018 Standard Britannia design ☐
☑ 2018 Bicentenary of Mary Shelley's
    "Frankenstein" ☐
☑ 2018 Journey to Armistice ☐
☐ 2018 Centenary of the RAF ☐
    2018 250th Anniversary of Captain Cook's
☐   "Voyage of Discovery" — I ☐
☑ 2019 Wedgwood ☐
☐ 2019 Samuel Pepys ☐
    2019 75th Anniversary of D-Day ☐
☐ 2019 Captain Cook — II ☐

ONE POUND (£1)

1983 Royal Arms ×4 ✓

1984 Scottish Thistle ☐

1985 Welsh Leek ☐

1986 Northern Ireland Flax ☐

1987 English Oak ☐

1988 Crowned Shield ☐

1989 Scottish Thistle ☐

1990 Welsh Leek ☐

1991 Northern Ireland Flax ☐

1992 English Oak ☐

1993 Royal Arms ☐

1994 Scottish Lion ☐

1995 Welsh Dragon ☐

1996 Northern Ireland Celtic Cross ☐

1997 English Lions ☐

1998 Royal Arms ☐

1999 Scottish Lion ☐

2000 Welsh Dragon ☐

2001 Northern Ireland Celtic Cross ✓

2002 English Lions ☐

2003 Royal Arms ☐

2004 Forth Railway Bridge ☐

2005 Menai Bridge ☐

2006 Egyptian Arch ☐

2007 Gateshead Millennium Bridge ☐

2008 Royal Arms ☐

2008 Uncrowned Shield ☐

2009 Uncrowned Shield ☐

2010 Uncrowned Shield ☐

2010 City Series (London) ☐

2010 City Series (Belfast) ☐

2011 Uncrowned Shield ☐

2011 City Series (Cardiff) ☐

2011 City Series (Edinburgh) ☐

2012 Uncrowned Shield ☐

2013 Uncrowned Shield ☐

2013 Floral Series (England) ☐

2013 Floral Series (Wales) ☐

2014 Uncrowned Shield ☐

2014 Floral Series (Scotland) ☐

2014 Floral Series (Northern Ireland) ☐

2015 Uncrowned Shield ☐

2015 Uncrowned Shield with New Portrait ☐

2015 Heraldic Royal Arms ☐

2016 The Last Round Pound with representations of the beasts of England, Scotland, Wales and Northern Ireland ☐

2017 Bi-metallic 12-sided Nations reverse ☐

2018 Bi-metallic 12-sided Nations reverse ☐

2019 Bi-metallic 12-sided Nations reverse ☐

FIFTY PENCE (50p)

1969 Britannia ☐

1970 Britannia ☐

1973 Accession to EEC ☐

1976 Britannia ☐

1977 Britannia ☐

1978 Britannia ☐

1979 Britannia ☐

1980 Britannia ✓

1981 Britannia ☐

1982 Britannia ☐

1983 Britannia ☐

1985 Britannia ☐

1992/93 Presidency of the European Council ☐

1994 50th Anniversary of the Normandy Landings ☐

1997 Britannia ☐

1998 Britannia ☐

1998 Presidency and 25th Anniversary of EU entry ☐

1998 50th Anniversary of the NHS ☐

1999 Britannia ☐

2000 Britannia ☐

2000 150th Anniversary of Public Libraries ✓

2001 Britannia ☐

2002 Britannia ☐

2003 Britannia ☐

2003 Centenary of the Suffragette Movement ☐

2004 Britannia ☐

2004 Anniversary of Roger Bannister's 4-minute mile ☐

2005 Britannia ☐

2005 250th Anniversary of Samuel Johnson and the Dictionary ✓

2006 Britannia ☐

2006 The Victoria Cross, The Award ☐

2006 The Victoria Cross, Heroic Acts ☐

2007 Britannia ✓

2007 Centenary of the Scout Movement ☐

2008 Britannia ☐

2008 New Shield Reverse ☐

2009 250th Anniversary of Kew Gardens ☐

2010 Centenary of Girl Guiding UK ☐

2011 50th Anniversary of the WWF ☐

2012 Shield ☐

2013 Shield ☐

2013 100th Anniversary of birth of Christopher Ironside ✓

2013 Centenary of the Birth of Benjamin Britten ☐

2014 Shield ☐

2014 XXth Commonwealth Games ☐

2015 Shield ☐

2015 75th Anniversary of the Battle of Britain ☐

2015 Shield, New portrait ☐

2016 950th Anniversary of the Battle of Hastings ☐

2016 Team GB for Rio Olympics ☐

2017 375th Anniversary of Sir Isaac Newton's birth ☐

2018 Anniversary of the Representation of the People Act ✓

2011 Olympic & Paralympic Sports Issues:

Aquatics—Head clear of lines ☐

—Head with lines (under water) ☐

Archery ☐

Athletics ☐

Badminton ✓

Basketball ☐

Boccia ✓

Boxing	☐ 1995	☐
Canoeing	☐ 1996	☑
Cycling	☐ 1997	☑
Equestrian	☐ 1998 New portrait	☑
Fencing	☐ 1999	☐
Football	☐ 2000	☐
Goalball	☐ 2001	☑
Gymnastics	☐ 2002	☐
Handball	☐ 2003	☐
Hockey	☐ 2004	☐
Judo	☐ 2005	☐
Modern Pentathlon	☐ 2006	☐
Rowing	☐ 2007	☐
Sailing	☐ 2008	☐
Shooting	☐ 2008 New reverse, date on obverse	☐
Table Tennis	☐ 2008—paired with old obverse (no date)	☐
Taekwondo	☐ 2009	☑
Tennis	☐ 2010	☐
Triathlon	☐ 2011	☐
Volleyball	☐ 2012	☑
Weightlifting	☐ 2013	☑
Wheelchair Rugby	☐ 2014	☐
Wrestling	☐ 2015	☐
2016 Peter Rabbit and the Author	☐ 2015 New portrait	☐
2016 Peter Rabbit	☐ 2016	☑
2016 Jemima Puddle-Duck	☐ 2017	☐
2016 Mrs. Tiggy-Winkle	☑ 2018	☐
2016 Squirrel Nutkin	☐ 2019	☐
2017 Peter Rabbit	☑	

TEN PENCE (10p)

2017 Mr. Jeremy Fisher	☐	
2017 Tom Kitten	☐ 1968	☐
2017 Benjamin Bunny	☑ 1969	☐
2018 Peter Rabbit	☐ 1970	☐
2018 Flopsy Bunny	☐ 1971	☐
2018 The Tailor of Gloucester	☐ 1973	☐
2018 Mrs. Tittlemouse	☐ 1974	☐
2018 Paddington Bear at Paddington Station	☑ 1975	☑
2018 Paddington Bear at Buckingham Palace	☐ 1976	☐
2018 The Snowman	☐ 1977	☐
2019 The Gruffalo	☐ 1979	☐
2019 Stephen Hawking	☐ 1980	☐
2019 Peter Rabbit	☐ 1981	☐
2019 Paddington Bear at the Tower	☑ 1985 New portrait	☐
2019 Paddington Bear at St. Paul's	☑ 1992 Size reduced	☐
	1995	☐
	1996	☐

TWENTY PENCE (20P)

1982	☑ 1997	☐
1983	☑ 1998 New portrait	☐
1984	☐ 2000	☑
1985 New portrait	☐ 2001	☐
1987	☐ 2002	☐
1988	☐ 2003	☐
1989	☐ 2004	☐
1990	☐ 2005	☑
1991	☐ 2006	☐
1992	☐ 2007	☐
1992	☐ 2008	☐
1993	☐ 2008 New reverse	☐
1994	☐ 2009	☐

2010	☐	Village		☐
2011	☑	World Wide Web		☐
2012	☑	X marks the spot		☐
2013	☑	Yeoman		☐
2014	☑	Zebra crossing		☐
2015	☐			
2015 New portrait	☑			
2016	☐	**FIVE PENCE (5p)**		
2017	☐	1968		☐
2018	☐	1969		☐
2018 Alphabet series:		1970		☐
Angel of the North	☐	1971		☐
James Bond	☐	1975		☐
Cricket	☐	1977		☐
Double-decker bus	☐	1978		☐
English breakfast	☐	1979		☐
Fish and chips	☐	1980		☐
Greenwich Mean Time	☐	1987 New portrait		☐
Houses of Parliament	☐	1988		☐
Ice cream	☐	1989		☐
Jubilee	☐	1990 Size reduced		☑
King Arthur	☐	1991		☐
Loch Ness	☐	1992		☐
Mackintosh	☐	1994		☐
NHS	☐	1995		☑
Oak tree	☐	1996		☐
Post box	☐	1997		☐
Queueing	☐	1998 New portrait		☐
Robin	☐	1999		☐
Stonehenge	☐	2000		☐
Tea	☐	2001		☐
Union Flag	☐	2002		☐
Village	☐	2003		☐
World Wide Web	☐	2004		☐
X marks the spot	☐	2005		☐
Yeoman	☐	2006		☐
Zebra crossing	☐	2007		☐
2019 Alphabet series:		2008		☐
Angel of the North	☐	2008 New reverse		☐
James Bond	☐	2009		☐
Cricket	☐	2010		☐
Double-decker bus	☐	2011		☐
English breakfast	☐	2012		☐
Fish and chips	☐	2013		☑
Greenwich Mean Time	☐	2014		☐
Houses of Parliament	☐	2015		☐
Ice cream	☐	2015 New portrait		☐
Jubilee	☐	2016		☐
King Arthur	☐	2017		☐
Loch Ness	☐	2018		☐
Mackintosh	☐	2019		☐
NHS	☐			
Oak tree	☐	**TWO PENCE (2p)**		
Post box	☐	1971		☐
Queueing	☐	1975		☐
Robin	☐	1976		☐
Stonehenge	☐	1977		☐
Tea	☐	1978		☑
Union Flag	☐	1979		☐

1980	☐
1981	☐
1982 Legend changed to TWO PENCE	☐
1983	☐
1983 Error NEW instead of TWO	☐
1984	☐
1985 New portrait	☐
1986	☐
1987	☐
1988	☐
1989	☐
1990	☐
1991	☐
1992	☐
1992	☐
1993	☐
1994	☐
1995	☐
1996	☐
1997	☐
1998 New portrait	☐
1998 Bronze	☐
1999	☐
2000	☐
2001	☐
2002	☐
2003	☐
2004	☐
2005	☐
2006	☐
2007	☐
2008	☐
2008 New reverse	☐
2009	☐
2010	☐
2011	☐
2012	☐
2013	☐
2014	☐
2015	☐
2015 New portrait	☐
2016	☐
2017	☐

ONE PENNY (1p)

1971	☐
1973	☐
1974	☐
1975	☑
1976	☐
1977	☐
1978	☑
1979	☐
1980	☐
1981	☐
1982 Legend changed to ONE PENNY	☐
1983	☐
1984	☐

1985 New portrait	☐
1986	☐
1987	☐
1988	☐
1989	☐
1990	☐
1991	☐
1992 Copper-plated steel	☐
1992 Bronze	☐
1993	☐
1994	☐
1995	☐
1996	☐
1997	☐
1998 New portrait	☐
1999	☐
2000	☐
2001	☐
2002	☐
2003	☐
2004	☐
2005	☐
2006	☐
2007	☐
2008	☐
2008 New reverse	☑
2009	☐
2010	☐
2011	☐
2012	☐
2013	☐
2014	☐
2015	☐
2015 New portrait	☐
2016	☐
2017	☐

HALF PENNY (1/2p)

1971	☐
1973	☐
1974	☐
1975	☐
1976	☐
1977	☐
1978	☐
1979	☐
1980	☐
1981	☐
1982 Legend changed from NEW PENNY to HALF PENNY	☐
1983	☐
1984 (the last one ever, only found in Year Sets)	☐

NOTE: This listing also includes those coins originally issued only in sets or special packs.